Realistic Hope

The Family Survival Guide for Facing

Alcoholism and Other Addictions

Also by P. Casey Arrillaga

Books

Mommy's Getting Sober

Spirituality for People Who Hate Spirituality

Podcast

Addiction and the Family

Website

CaseyAuthor.com

Realistic Hope

The Family Survival Guide for Facing

Alcoholism and Other Addictions

P. Casey Arrillaga, LCSW, LCDC

Recovery Tree Publishing
recoverytreemedia.com
recoverytreebooks@gmail.com

ISBN: 978-1-7379815-0-3

Cover design by Barry Wood
www.otheroom.com

Interior design by Di Freeze
www.freezetimemedia.com

Author photo by Kira Arrillaga

Dedicated with love to Kira and Jess

Contents

Introduction

Beginning on the Road of Realistic Hope

Alcoholism, or any other form of addiction*, is a terrible thing to happen to a family, and if it is happening to your family then I am truly sorry. What I want to offer you is hope. I will not give false promises that if you just make all the right moves and avoid all the wrong ones then your loved one will get and stay sober for life. What I can say with confidence is that things can get better than they are right now, and you can feel better than you do.

There is no one-size-fits-all answer, but any family can learn to not only survive but also grow and even thrive when faced with the many challenges posed by addiction. How is this possible? In short, through finding realistic hope. I cannot overemphasize the importance of this idea. When

*A note about the terms "alcoholism" and "addiction." Alcoholism is simply a term for addiction to alcohol, so alcoholism will be included in the general category of addiction throughout this book. Alcohol is a drug by any scientific measure, so any discussion of drugs in this book can be assumed to include alcohol. While the vast majority of research is done on addiction to drugs, there is growing awareness of behavioral addictions, such as addiction to food,[1] gambling,[2] shopping,[3] or sex.[4] I believe the suggestions in this book will apply just as much for families of people with such addictions.

1

family members lose hope, the family situation can quickly turn into one of anger, separation, tears, and looking for someone to blame. Yet when a family clings to an unrealistic hope that addiction is just a passing phase, that they can love their family member into good health and good behavior, or that the family can handle this on their own, they often find themselves in just as much distress because these ideas and efforts usually fail.

Families in either situation can find themselves trying the same things over and over again, confused and frustrated when they keep getting the same results or worse. They are often tempted to throw their hands in the air and give up on their loved one, rather than learning to set and keep effective boundaries. They may be tempted to blame every problem in the family on the addiction, rather than seeing that the addiction may only be exacerbating rather than causing many of the family's issues. If you are reading this book, I will assume you don't want to fall into these traps or any of the others laid out in the following chapters. Instead, you want realistic hope.

My goal is to offer that hope through the things I have learned in my professional and personal life, along with both current scientific findings and practical clinical tools. Throughout this book, I draw on my experience of leading hundreds of workshops for family members of clients at treatment centers and seeing many people start to heal and

grow individually and together. Additionally, I draw on my experience of growing up around addiction, having been in active addiction and now recovery myself, having enabled addiction and then supported recovery in my spouse, and grappling with the real possibility of losing our child to mental illness. If you're wondering how this last part relates, I found that my daughter's struggles with mental illness led to many of the same dilemmas and ultimately the same solutions as the struggles other family members have with addiction. Through all of this, I have seen what this disease can do within a family from many perspectives, and I want to do what I can to help you find the hope and recovery that I and so many others have been able to enjoy.

If this sounds good, then let's look at how you can find realistic hope for your family like I did for mine.

One way my family started to find realistic hope was through learning the reality about addiction rather than going by popular opinion or "common sense" assumptions. This meant getting scientific facts, learning about contributing factors, and facing the sometimes-uncomfortable truths about how we all make decisions. As I went on this journey, I was amazed at how many things I thought I knew about addiction turned out to be wrong. This faulty knowledge contributed to my emotional pain. As I learned the facts and shared them with my family, we moved beyond shame and blame and into compassion and solution.

We learned the importance of loving honesty, not only from the person with addiction but also from every member of the family. We came to see that everyone in the family needs to recover from the effects of addiction, rather than thinking we would all be "fixed" if the person with the addiction got better. We learned that the most helpful thing anyone can do for their family members is to work on themselves. We moved out of isolation and stopped trying to beat addiction on our own.

The first chapters of this book cover these concepts, along with a detailed guide on what to expect from various types of addiction treatment. The later chapters deal with practical concepts and skills that have helped many families survive and thrive. These include: effective communication and boundaries, codependency, enabling and rescuing vs. helping, family dynamics and roles that people often take on when the family is stressed, and how to create greater happiness no matter how the addiction is going. The book concludes with an appendix of resources where help can be found, as well as a reference list of the studies cited in each chapter.

Much of this is based on observing which things have seemed most helpful in the family workshops I have led. All of the information in this book has helped my family, and I hope it can now help yours.

Chapter 1

Addiction: What It Is and What It Isn't

In order for your family to get through all the difficulties surrounding addiction, we need to talk about what addiction is and what it isn't. I have seen many families, including mine, spin their wheels and engage in a lot of pointless conflict born out of misunderstanding. In my family, we would ask each other, "Why can't you stop?!?" We grew frustrated and resentful, wondering why our love was not enough and how someone could know they were hurting everyone yet keep going anyway. We sometimes had outbursts of anger, but in other times quietly resigned ourselves to things staying this way forever. As we moved into recovery, we still carried a lot of misunderstanding and ignorance around the condition we were trying to overcome. We found that knowing the facts about addiction allowed everyone in the family a greater chance of finding realistic hope and opened the door to a measure of peace in circumstances that otherwise lend themselves to chaos and pain.

What Addiction Is

Addiction is a chronic, relapsing, and potentially deadly brain disease that strikes hardest below the level of conscious thought, in the part of the brain that has the strongest influence on how we make decisions. If this sounds scary, it should. No one likes to think of a loved one having such a condition, but the science around this is solid, so we need to have a clear-eyed view of what we are up against.

To say addiction is chronic means that someone with an addiction will likely always be vulnerable to addiction, but like many controllable chronic conditions (think diabetes), if they keep up the proper actions, they can live full and happy lives. Addiction is a relapsing condition because, like other chronic conditions, if someone with an addiction stops taking the prescribed actions, they will likely see a return to previous symptoms and their condition often deteriorates from there. Most people know that addiction is potentially deadly in the sense that people with addiction are vulnerable to things like overdose or liver failure, but it is easy to underestimate how many other deaths are linked to addiction. Violent death, suicide, and fatal accidents are all more likely under the influence of drugs. According to the World Health Organization, 3.3 million deaths each year are attributable to alcohol consumption alone.[1] People with behavioral addictions rarely die from the direct effects, but

many take their own lives out of despair, leaving behind grieving loved ones who wonder what possibly could have driven their family member to such an act.

Addiction is also referred to by many as a family disease. Almost anyone who is in relationship with a family member or other loved one with addiction is negatively affected. The entire family can find itself organized around the addiction, trying to fight it, hide it, or hide from it. This can lead to serious psychological harm and painful intergenerational patterns. Research shows that family members of someone with an addiction are more vulnerable to chronic health conditions, suicide, PTSD, high risk behaviors, victimization, unintended pregnancies, lower life achievement, shorter life expectancies, and a greater chance of falling prey to addiction themselves.[2]

In short, addiction is a force of destruction, and often a killer.

What Addiction Isn't

Addiction is not a lack of morals, a lack of willpower, a sign of parental failure, or the result of simply having hung out with the wrong crowd. It is certainly not a choice, it is not anybody's fault, and it is not a problem to be solved by shaming and blaming. Most importantly, it is not a hopeless condition. While addiction is often mistaken for these things, families cannot afford such misunderstandings. How we define a problem will define the solutions that we seek. Thus, a simplistic misunderstanding of addiction will lead the family to attempt solutions that rarely get the desired results. Such misunderstanding can also set up unrealistic expectations, leading to further pain and conflict.

Addiction is not a lack of morals. If it were, then moral instruction might be the solution. Families and societies have been trying this for thousands of years. You would expect it to have done the trick by now. It is true that some of us need to rediscover our moral compass once we get sober, mostly due to having lived in a state of emotional underdevelopment and selfishness in order to survive, but moralizing to people in the grip of active addiction is usually fruitless.

If addiction were evidence of an intrinsic lack of morals, then the condition would be hopeless, since moral fiber is hard to manufacture in someone who doesn't already have it. If it were a lack of morals, we should expect to see people in recovery turning out to be amoral. Instead, we see people recovering and becoming their best selves as they embrace spirituality and service to others. They aren't learning to fake it well; they are recovering who they really are. Additionally, if addiction were the result of a lack of morals, people with addiction would have no regrets about their actions. Instead, we consistently see that people with addiction are filled with guilt and shame when they first get sober.

I know I certainly was. While in active addiction, I worked hard to justify my addictive actions to myself. Despite my best efforts, I knew deep inside that those actions took me far from who I wanted to be. If I had no morals, I could never have thought this. I also found that when I was not in the grip of the compulsion to act out, I was compassionate, helpful, kind, and a generally good person. As one of my mentors in recovery has often said, we aren't bad people trying to be good, we are sick people trying to be well.

Addiction is not a lack of willpower. It actually takes tremendous willpower to sustain an addiction. Family, friends, society, the financial cost, and the law all can pose serious opposition. A person with an addiction must exert willpower to overcome any of these things that gets between them and the next fix. It has been said that people in the grip of addiction are some of the hardest working people you will meet, yet they get some of the worst returns for their labors. The problem they have is that their willpower is hijacked and put in service of sustaining the addictive behavior at all costs.

Addiction is not a sign of parental failure. Many of us grew up in a culture that believes that any outcome of the child should be laid at the feet of the parents. I certainly went for the bait on this one. I believed that if my daughter was doing well, then that would be proof that I was a good parent. When her brain crashed emotionally in her early teens, I focused on her recovery not only as something good for her, but also as a way to rescue my self-image as a good parent. When it should have been apparent that there was going to be no quick fix for her mental illness, I still pushed her to just be more normal and snap out of it. Why couldn't she see the logic of behaving differently? It was not immediately obvious to me that I was blaming myself for her condition, and thus my pushing was, in part, a way to soothe this self-blaming. If she felt better, then I could, too. Ultimately, I joined one of the fellowships for family members of people with addiction, not because she had an addiction, but because I couldn't let go of my need to control her outcomes. The fellowship showed me how to let someone I love have their own journey. I learned to let go of my attachment to what I wanted for her and instead love her as she is. As I gave up the idea that her struggles were my failure, it also took pressure off her to recover for me. Instead, she could decide to do so, or not, for herself.

I have watched many parents go through a similar journey when their child has an addiction. They look for something they must have done wrong and what they can do to fix it. While all parents make mistakes, addiction is not so simply caused. I suspect that many of us looked for what we did wrong not only because society told us we failed, but also because it gives a twisted sense of control. If I could find what I did wrong, then I might be able to do something about it. If I face the reality that the addiction is not my fault, then I may feel powerless instead. As we will see in later chapters, this admission of powerlessness is often the beginning of freedom, but this is a step that scares many people. Like the person with addiction, many family members have to try everything else before they embrace the solution.

Addiction is not the result of simply having hung out with the wrong crowd. It is true that many of us with addictions had help getting into trouble. Just as with recovery, there are people who have walked the path of addiction before us who can show us the way. I had friends who turned me on to addictive behaviors, but none of them made the choice for me to embrace these things. Indeed, they were sometimes initially amused then later alarmed at my passion for what they showed me. As I embraced "the dark side," I gravitated towards people who supported and even encouraged my addictive behavior, sometimes thinking they were the only ones who understood me. In turn, I encouraged others' extreme behaviors as a way to not feel like such a freak. If my old friends wanted no part of my obsessive-compulsive behavior around addiction, I would spend less time with them and share less of myself. Thus, I eventually found I was only around people who either supported my addiction or who had no idea it was happening.

From the outside, it may have seemed like I was corrupted by negative influences, but I was really seeking them out. Additionally, while the people who loved me may have thought, "If only Casey wasn't hanging out with that person he'd be doing better," the other person's loved ones were likely thinking, "If only my loved one wasn't hanging out with Casey, they'd be doing better." They all may have been right, but when we are looking to escape ourselves, we seek out people who can both show us how and then accept us when we embrace that escape.

Addiction is not a choice. Most people choose to try alcohol or other drugs at some point in their lives, perhaps to change their emotional state, to relax, or just because it's what everyone does. This isn't the same as choosing to be addicted. Nobody says, "I can't wait until my life is spinning out of control. I can't want to hate myself for what I'm doing and keep doing it anyway." Some of us are walking into a biological and psychological trap when we first try drugs or extreme behaviors. This trap may slowly lure us in or spring shut at the first use, but none of us chooses to be trapped.

Addiction is not anybody's fault any more than diabetes or cancer are anybody's fault. This flies in the face of common sense, which tells us that the person with the addiction is to blame for their choices and behavior, but addiction is a disorder primarily in the part of the brain that motivates our choices and behavior. It is often fueled by unresolved psychological pain that most people would not think to associate with addictive behavior, and many people cannot stick with their choice to stop until that pain is sufficiently addressed.

Addiction is not fixed through shame and blame. If shame and blame got us sober, we all would have been sober long ago, because those of us with addictions are already great at shaming and blaming ourselves. I have worked with thousands of people suffering from addiction and they universally feel shame about their addiction and blame themselves for their predicament. Some of us hide our shame behind the bravado of blaming everyone and everything else, but this just turns out to be a way to deflect from the massive shame underneath.

In my case, I grew up as a shameful person, and felt certain I was worth less than everyone around me. I blamed myself for everything that I thought had gone wrong in my life, including being sexually abused, being put up for adoption, and having erratic and sometimes violent behavior that I couldn't explain. Addiction provided a means of escape from my painful feelings but also led to more shame and blame from myself and others, keeping me in a seemingly endless cycle. I eventually embraced addiction as my secret identity, certain I had found a solution to all the feelings I couldn't resolve, but this also meant embracing the self-shaming. I was 10 years old at this point. If shame or blame was going to help, I would have started getting better then, because I was getting plenty of those things from myself and some of the people around me. Instead, shame was more fuel for the fire, and I slid downhill for another 20 years.

To avoid such outcomes for you and your family, let's take a look at what is scientifically known about addiction.

What We Know So Far

Addiction has been with us as a species for as far back as we can see. Many of our oldest religious texts warn about overuse of drugs such as alcohol, and there would be no need for this if our ancestors hadn't been overdoing it already. Pretty much every society uses substances of one kind or another, such as fermented plants (alcohol), the opium poppy, the coca leaf (cocaine), khat, and various hallucinogens (mushrooms, peyote). As our knowledge of chemistry has improved, so too has our ability to refine and mimic such natural substances, resulting in more and more potent drugs (distilled liquor, heroin, crack cocaine, fentanyl, LSD, benzodiazepines, methamphetamine, ecstasy, "bath salts," etc.). It is hard to say whether addiction has become more common or just more commonly admitted, but the demand for professional treatment and mutual self-help fellowships does not seem to be slowing down any time soon. Both politicians and the medical community talk about the public health crisis addiction poses. It is hard to find any family that has not been affected either directly or through someone they know, although many families isolate themselves from potential support out of shame or ignorance, probably leading to underestimation of the true extent of the problem.

Behavioral addictions (sometimes called "process addictions") have probably also been with us for all of our history. They too seem to have increased in incidence as modern food production makes calories easier, more plentiful, and cheaper than at any other time in human history; the Internet makes gambling available 24 hours a day from anywhere; smartphones make casual sex partners available through various apps while providing a practically limitless supply of free pornography; and advertising and social media set standards of how much must be spent, often on credit, to look good and feel complete. The evidence for an increase in awareness of behavioral addictions is bolstered by ever-increasing membership in recovery groups dedicated to such conditions. These include fellowships specific to food addiction, gambling addiction, sex and love addiction, and compulsive spending. While some may scoff, in 2013 the DSM 5, which is the standard text for mental health diagnosis in the United States, acknowledged Gambling Disorder as a valid diagnosis for the first time, and in 2018 the World Health Organization recognized Compulsive Sexual Behavior Disorder as more than a joke in a raunchy movie. Both of these diagnoses have critics in the mental health community and beyond, but the thousands of sufferers who are seeking treatment and mutual self-help fellowships for these addictions are not waiting for professional consensus about their disease. Their pain, and that of those closest to them, demands help now. The fact that sufferers seem to be aided by the same techniques and support that have most successfully addressed drug addictions speaks to the idea that behavioral addictions are basically the same condition in another form. As we explore what is happening in the brain, reasons for saying this may become clear. We'll begin our exploration by looking at the brain physiology involved in how we make choices, which is vital to understanding addiction.

The Power of Choice?

How could someone we love could make such terrible choices? How could they be dishonest with us and do things that not only baffle us but also hurt themselves and those around them? To answer this, we need to look at how human beings make decisions. We like to think that most of the time we make choices based on reason and that our decisions are logically well-justified. This is not so. In fact, we make most of our decisions below the level of conscious thought, based more on emotion than logic.[3] Emotion, in turn, is often inspired by deeply held beliefs that we may not even realize we have.[4] These emotions and beliefs alter the way we see our surroundings and how we interpret everything that happens both inside and outside of ourselves. While we often do not realize or even question these deeper motivations, we are adept at rationalizing and justifying them.

The two strongest emotional motivators we have are fear and pleasure. Both emotions start deep in the brain*. An area of the brain called the *limbic system* is fundamental to both emotions, and this system filters and makes basic judgments about every experience we have before our conscious mind even knows we have experienced anything at all. Fear tells us that what we are experiencing seems like a threat to our survival. Pleasure tells us that what we are experiencing seems like something that will enhance our survival. In other words, the limbic system is deeply concerned with our survival.[5]

* I am simplifying this discussion of brain anatomy and the neurochemical processes of addiction because there are already many fine descriptions available. For those who wish more detail, I recommend the book "Never Enough" by Judith Grisel, the documentary "Pleasure Unwoven" By Kevin McCauley, and from my own podcast, Addiction and the Family, "Episode 5: Addiction and the Brain" as excellent starting points.

This is essential for our discussion, because it is the limbic system that is most dramatically hijacked by addiction. A person's deepest and strongest subconscious motivations are altered to think that the addictive behavior is vital to their survival. Because our brain is structured to place our survival at highest priority in all but the most extraordinary circumstances, the limbic system can override other brain structures when sufficiently aroused. This may help explain why a person with an addiction can know and verbalize that they need to quit (or at least slow down) and then turn around and do exactly what they swore they no longer wanted to do. The conscious mind knows without a doubt that the addictive behavior is causing more trouble than it is worth. The conscious mind can look into the future and see that things are likely to only get worse. The limbic system, on the other hand, cannot see a full minute into the future. It wants what it wants, and it wants it now. This is especially true when it is strongly activated, and addictive behaviors including drug use are things that fire the limbic system up quite dramatically. Drugs of abuse do this by mimicking or amplifying the chemical messages that we rely on for all brain function, and other addictive behaviors distort these chemical messages by ramping up the natural reward systems around such survival mechanisms as eating, sex, acquiring things, and winning.

The limbic system is also concerned with forming long-term memories, which means that when something seems essential to survival, memories will be formed to guide future behaviors. Drugs of abuse hit the limbic system so hard that a permanent memory may be created that says that the drug is the best survival move ever. Similarly, when nominal survival behaviors such as overeating or experiencing the rush of early love are taken to repeated extremes, the brain may encode these as the solution to every emotional problem. This is one reason we say that people with addiction are always vulnerable to relapse unless they engage in regular recovery efforts. Essentially, someone with an addiction must always offer their brain a better solution than the addictive behavior, or the old solution may be sought once again. The limbic system ensures that this will happen no matter how much the logical mind knows that the old solution is likely to lead to pain and destruction.

Offering a better solution is not as easy as it sounds. Once the limbic system has gotten a taste for the overload that drugs or extreme behaviors provide, it is hard to give them up. This is not only because day-to-day life does not provide the same levels of stimulation, but also because after repeated dosing, the affected brain cells try to avoid being overloaded by reducing the pleasure and motivation they can feel on average. Once the cells have made these changes, the brain is left in a state where it feels undernourished and demands more stimulation whenever the addictive drugs or behaviors are not present. This leads the limbic system to go off like an alarm that the rest of the brain cannot ignore. If you have ever challenged someone's addiction and gotten a reaction like you are threatening their survival, this is why.

Once the limbic alarm has been set off, the conscious mind will naturally rationalize a return to addictive behaviors, often saying, such things as "Just one more time," "I deserve it," or, "I don't care about the consequences anymore, I just need relief." After the limbic system has been satisfied, regret and shame often set in, leaving the person with confusion about how they could possibly have done the things they did. After enough repetitions of this pattern, many tell themselves they must be horrible, weak, and/or shameful people. These negative emotions put further pressure on the limbic system, making it more vulnerable to going off again, trapping the victim in a vicious cycle. In the face of this, some give up hope and resign themselves to the life of an active addict, perhaps masking this with bravado or nonchalance, telling the people they love to back off and let them "be who they are." They may look for someone to blame for their seemingly hopeless condition, and the people around them make good targets.

Anyone who has not experienced losing the power of rational choice may find it hard to empathize with those who have. Sometimes the family members who are the angriest are those who have abused substances or behaviors in the past and were able to stop on their own. For them, especially, it can be hard to see that everyone does not start on a level playing field when it comes to addiction.

Heightened Risk

Many people are particularly vulnerable to addiction before they ever try drugs of abuse or push potentially addictive behaviors to extremes. This is because genetic predispositions, environmental factors, and psychological vulnerabilities leave some people much more prone to addiction that others. We will look at each of these factors in turn, and then how they interact to create a picture of addiction vulnerability.

Genetics are currently estimated to be about 60% of the risk factor for addiction, although there does not appear to be a single addiction gene. Genetic risk factors are diverse and include such genetically-influenced traits as a tendency toward impulsive behavior[6], how various drugs are metabolized[7], vulnerability to other brain conditions[8], and perhaps most important, the inability to experience sufficient reward and well-being naturally from normal behaviors.[9] Genetics are not fate, however. They may instead be seen as potential and tendency. In fact, our genome is very responsive to the environment, with various genes turning themselves on and off based on what is going on around and within us. Thus, family members who carry many of the same genetics will have various outcomes around addiction due to having different life experiences and different psychological reactions to those experiences. A colleague of mine offers a modern parable of two twin brothers with an alcoholic father. One grows up and drinks uncontrollably, saying, "With a father like that, what else would you expect?" The other abstains from alcohol for life, saying, "With a father like that, what else would you expect?"

What might tip someone in one direction or another? There are many environmental influences that can affect addiction risk. Some of the better-known include peer group, family and local cultural attitudes towards use of alcohol and other drugs, media messages, and availability. One risk factor stands out above all others, though, and that is trauma. For our purposes, trauma may be defined as any experience that leaves a person feeling less safe in the world. This means that it is not the event itself, but a person's reaction to it, that defines how traumatic the event is. I like to say that trauma is in the eye of the beholder. Therefore, trauma may come as a single big event that anyone would recognize as having a profound impact, or it may be a long series of smaller events that chip away at the person's sense of safety until that person is habitually reacting to the world with fear. Big traumas include such things as abuse, neglect, violence, or life-threatening events. Big traumas can also come from life-saving events such as being adopted or undergoing childhood surgery. This doesn't mean that such things shouldn't happen. It means that we have to acknowledge that no matter how good these things are in the eyes of the adults, to the child they may be frightening enough that they no longer feel safe.

Some examples of the less-acknowledged "smaller" repetitive traumas include growing up around addiction in its various manifestations, being a repeated victim of bullying, regularly being put down, moving often as a child, constant family conflict, living in a dangerous neighborhood, repeatedly experiencing racism and/or sexism, a string of academic failures with or without a learning disability, and anything else that regularly leaves a person feeling threatened, hopeless, less than others, or constantly on guard.

Least recognized of all is the trauma that results from hurting others, betraying one's own values, and the horror and shame of becoming the worst version of oneself. These are experiences that are common in addiction. In my active addiction, I constantly told myself I would do better, and I wanted to be a better version of myself, but I seemed powerless to stop my antisocial behaviors when they benefitted my addiction. This left me with a very low impression of my own character despite knowing I would rather help people than hurt them, and that I would like to be trustworthy and kind.

Many family members find that if they are honest with themselves, they have had parallel experiences of being traumatized due to the addiction. For some, this will include seeing themselves be hurtful and falling short of their own values.

Reactions to trauma are not uniform or always predictable. The younger a person is when they experience trauma, the more profound its effect is likely to be. Their reaction will also be influenced by such genetic factors as a tendency toward anxiety, depression, impulsiveness, anger, or pessimism[10]. This means that a person who has suffered trauma may look at the world and themselves through the lens of that trauma from that point forward, often remaining constantly vigilant for any sign that the traumatic experience might be repeated. Thus, they subconsciously shape their behaviors to avoid getting hurt again. It often seems that traumatized people seek each other out without realizing they are doing so. They simply relate better to others who have gone through similar experiences, as most of us do. Unfortunately, the commonalities of unresolved trauma can lead to people replaying their issues together, which can create frustration and further trauma. Saddest of all is the fact that predatory people may pick up on the telltale signs of these behavior and attitude changes, often leading to repeated victimization of traumatized individuals.

All of this can result in great amounts of internal suffering that can go unnoticed by anyone else for years or decades, and which even the sufferer may not consciously associate with the originating trauma. I've worked with many clients who say the same thing I said about my trauma reactions: "I've always been this way." It wasn't until I did my own deep trauma work that I realized that many of my most troublesome personality characteristics were really coping mechanisms. It took a lot of recovery and therapy to see that these traits were no longer necessary. Many people are impatient for quick results but also are scared to give up these familiar defenses. If this seems like a matter that logic should solve, remember that our emotional mind can override our logical mind when pain or the threat of pain is great enough.

This highlights the third set of risk factors: psychological risk factors. These are the mind's reactions to the combination of genes and environment. These psychological risk factors include low self-esteem, anxiety, depression, any other psychiatric disorder (e.g., bipolar or schizophrenia), alienation, hopelessness, feeling "terminally unique," grandiose thinking, impulsivity, and emotional sensitivity that can lead someone to try to shut the world or their own emotions out. These all can cut back on a sense of connection to others and the wider world. This increases risk for addiction because human beings thrive when they feel connected and suffer when they don't. Whenever people are suffering, they are more vulnerable to addiction.

Much of what happens at a treatment center, in individual and group counselling, and in recovery fellowships such as Twelve Step groups, deals with these psychological risk factors. Out of the all the risks, these are the ones most obviously able to be changed, and the ones for which people feel most responsible. We may not pick our environment and we certainly don't pick our genes, but we have more choice than we may realize about how we react to internal and external events. This doesn't mean these things are easy to change, just that it's possible to do so.

Finally, all of these risk factors influence each other. Our environment profoundly influences how our genes express, our genes profoundly influence our psychological reactions, and both of these influence the experiences we have. For instance, someone with a potential for depression who is spared triggering stressors may feel less joy than the average but may never become clinically depressed. Someone else with the same genes may run into the wrong experiences and find that depression starts to creep into their life in a way that is hard to shake. This, in turn, keeps them from socializing as much as their non-depressed peers, leading to a growing sense of hopelessness, which may in turn reinforce the genetic expression of depression. This creates a downward spiral that can feel overwhelming.

Then one day, someone comes along and says, "Drink this, smoke that, you'll feel better." Guess what? It works. They do feel better. That relief is harder to refuse after each use. If the person has genetics, life experiences, and psychological reactions that make them more vulnerable to addiction, they become more and more likely to reach a point where they can't stick with the decision to stop even when they want to.

To make matters worse, there is a particular phase of life when genetic, environmental, and psychological risk factors all converge.

A Most Dangerous Time

Adolescence, which is the biological and social transition from childhood to adulthood, is the greatest danger zone when it comes to starting an addiction. This stage of human development, which can begin as early as 8 years old and continues until about 25 years old, is when most people try drugs of abuse for the first time and may ramp up other potentially addictive behaviors. Let's review the list of environmental risk factors we made earlier: peer group, family and local cultural attitudes towards use of alcohol and other drugs, media messages, availability of alcohol and other drugs, and trauma. Each of these becomes more profound during adolescence. During this stage of life, a person's peer group challenges the primacy of family relationships for the first time, family and cultural attitudes are questioned, susceptibility to media messages is high, and drugs are available as never before. Some drug use, including drinking alcohol, is seen as a way to find acceptance, demonstrate adult capabilities, and relieve the enormous emotional pressures of adolescence. Meanwhile, the adolescent brain is making changes that leave a person willing to take greater risks in return for less certain rewards. Evolution may have favored these traits in order to push our foremothers and forefathers to explore the world and get pregnant more easily, but these same traits leave a person much more vulnerable to develop addictions.

The effects of trauma, which may have seemed minimal in younger childhood, are likely to spring up in new and disturbing ways as the brain undergoes the changes of adolescence. For instance, a person who has been though sexual abuse as a child may seem relatively normal until adolescence. Suddenly, they may become preoccupied with sex beyond the norms of their age and begin sexual activity earlier than their peers. They may seek as many partners as they can, including people outside of their appropriate age range. They may be willing to sacrifice their values and social standing in order to get one more sexual hit. They may become predatory or set themselves up as prey. These activities may come with or without extremes of emotional and romantic attachment.

All of this describes me as a preteen and teen, but I might have gone another way. Some people who had similar abuse withdraw from all sexual experience, focusing instead on extremes of romance and fantasy but not wanting to reopen their sexuality for fear of reexperiencing the pain of their early abuse. Still others avoid all sexual and romantic involvement, seeking safety that comes at the steep price of loneliness and internal alienation from other adolescents at the time of life when connection to peers is most important. While there are as many reactions to trauma as there are people who have endured it, the least likely outcome of all is to sail through with no ill effects and no discomfort. As the many risk factors for addiction converge, trauma adds its weight and the adolescent may embrace any available relief. Drugs and other addictive behaviors offer exactly that. Childhood pledges to "just say no" and parental warnings can't compete with this desperate need to feel better.

Remember the psychological risk factors that led to a greater sense of disconnection? Adolescents are particularly sensitive to feeling disconnected, and many of these risk factors come out in this time of life like no other. Some of the psychiatric conditions, such as schizophrenia, first start to manifest in late teens and early twenties, leading to both the inherent problems of the psychiatric disorder and the growing knowledge that the sufferer has something wrong that sets them apart, something most adolescents fear deeply.

In my case, a lifetime of feeling different, anxious, and angry hit a whole new level as I headed into middle school. It suddenly seemed paramount to find a way to fit in socially, yet I felt unable to do so. I already felt like a space traveler dropped onto the wrong planet. I was certain that any social situation would end up with me at the bottom of the pecking order. I tried to impress people with over-the-top behavior. I alienated people with my fear of rejection. To top it all off, I was angry because I felt this was all terribly unfair. Even when I suspected that I was the author of my own misery, I felt powerless over my compulsive attempts to be accepted. To cope with this, I took any addictive opportunity to escape, such as overeating, doing anything that produced adrenaline, sexual activity, voyeurism, and pornography when I could find it. I would lock myself in the bathroom to read science fiction and fantasy for so long that my mother suspected gastrointestinal problems. I took to eating breakfast with the boxes of cereal around me like a fortress while I played music through headphones and read a book at the same time, all in an attempt to make my reality go away. While I was initially scared to try alcohol and other drugs, this fear was eventually overridden by the strength of my desire to change the way I felt. I was embracing any means of escape, right at the stage of brain development when we form patterns and associations that last a lifetime.

This illustrates the fact that addiction does not start out as a problem, but instead shows up disguised as a solution. The sufferer cannot see, or perhaps refuses to believe, that this solution will later become a bigger problem than the ones it was meant to solve. By the time this becomes apparent, it is usually too late. The pathway has been formed and the association is indelibly burned into place.

Where, then, do we find hope?

Chapter 2

Building Hope

In my family, I was the first one to seek recovery. This is because my problems were the most obvious and they were getting worse. My life looked great from the outside, with a 10-year marriage, young child, good job, two cars in the garage of our house, respect in the community, clean legal record, dog, and a picket fence. What few suspected was that I was getting ready to lose everything on that list because I couldn't recognize, let alone control, my addiction. Despite all my efforts to keep my problem hidden, it had gotten to the point that it was all going to burst into the open because, like most addictions, it was steadily getting worse.

My wife and I had done weekly individual and couples counseling in the first six years of our marriage with a brilliant therapist and we learned incredibly useful tools for communication while working through many of our traumas and issues. What we didn't do was address our addictions because we couldn't see that we were addicted. We just thought we were cooler than everyone else and therefore entitled to our own standards of morality. Our therapist knew something was off, but I never gave her all the facts about what I was doing, and when she hinted at addiction as a possibility, I blew it off. As my wife's behavior became less outwardly destructive, mine went in the opposite direction.

The façade of my perfect life was crumbling as my actions ruined friendships and got people talking amongst themselves about what they saw wrong with me. Despite this, I still thought I could control things. Instead, I got worse and worse, and found it harder and harder to pretend like everything was okay. My wife finally confronted me, and I got honest about everything for the first time. Then she said the magic words, "I guess you'd better go find one of those meetings we keep hearing about." This was my entry into recovery.

When I started going to meetings of a local recovery fellowship, I was so focused on my struggles to get and stay sober that I never stopped to wonder whether anyone else in my family needed help. Therefore, I was quite surprised when three years into my journey, my wife announced that she needed to get into recovery for her own addiction. Through her bravery in this, we started to learn a common language of recovery. While it would be years before I would talk to our daughter about the family legacy of addiction, I knew we were offering her a chance to see recovery in action in her parents. We recognized that we had an opportunity to disrupt some of the family patterns that had weighed down the branches of both our family trees.

When she was a teenager, my daughter complained that it wasn't fair that my wife and I had meetings to go to where there were always supportive people, and steps in recovery we could take to guide us, while she felt little social support for her issues. I pointed out that our family histories thoroughly qualified her for membership in any of the recovery groups for families and friends of people with addiction. She had her doubts and I did my best not to push her. One day, however, she said she would give it a try. I had learned enough by that point to avoid showing too much excitement or approval. I just said I would take her to a meeting any time she wanted. She slowly embraced this idea and tried attending a local fellowship for quite a while before deciding that it wasn't for her. I felt some disappointment and fear at her decision because by then her life had been an anxious struggle for years, and her mental state had deteriorated into near-constant depression, regular suicidality, delusional thinking, and paranoia at times. I hoped that what had helped me would help her even though our symptoms looked different. When she continued to struggle, I grew to see that her recovery is just that: *her recovery*. It may not look like mine and I may not even recognize it when it's happening. The fact that she has any willingness to get better is a blessing. I feel gratitude that she has embraced therapy and that she discusses her problems with me when she sees fit. I prefer this to living in fear just because she doesn't get her support in the exact same ways as my wife and me.

Why am I telling you all this? To show some of the many ways that you can start to build realistic hope. In this chapter, I will talk about some of these avenues for hope, including finding your own recovery, recovery cascading in the family, finding support, using loving honesty, and getting out of the Identified Patient model.

Why Family Members Need Recovery

You may be thinking, "Why do I need recovery? I'm not the one with a problem!" That may be true, but if you are reading this book, I'm going to assume that you and others in your family have been affected by addiction. That means that everyone in the family needs to recover from the effects of that situation. As we saw in the previous section, you probably won't get very far by trying to force others to change, but you have a pretty good shot at getting yourself to start healing.

Sometimes we can't easily recognize all the ways we have been affected, so I'll list common reactions to living with addiction. Those who have been through the experience cite such things as[1]:

- isolation
- pervasive fear
- people-pleasing
- fear of anger and criticism
- compulsive activity
- victim mentality
- sense of responsibility to fix others
- guilt at healthy behavior
- guilt at keeping boundaries
- stuffing feelings
- extreme self-criticism
- overdependence on others
- feeling powerless over their own reactivity

Some people have seen themselves worrying about others' drinking, lying to cover for others, setting boundaries they don't keep, walking on eggshells, feeling embarrassed by others' behavior, isolating, feeling like failures because they can't get someone else to stop, and falling for the illusion that their problems would be solved if their loved one stopped using drugs.[2]

If you can see yourself in some of these things, then you have a basis to get your recovery going because the starting point for any solution is to recognize that a problem exists. If you feel like a compulsive fixer, and perhaps you grew up believing that this is your job, it can be both frustration and relief to see that there is really only one person you can work on fixing. You guessed it: that person is you.

Frustration at this idea can come because many of us like to think that our problems would be solved if other people would just behave and/or be okay, so it can feel difficult to think that we are the authors of our own unhappiness. It is easier to blame others, especially when they behave in ways that most people would agree are unacceptable, when they refuse to take accountability, or when they are remorseful but don't seem to change. Nonetheless we can see that blaming them and trying to get them to change has not led to anyone involved being happier, safer, or more content in the long run.

Frustration can also set in if we grew up believing we have to make sure the people around us are safe and okay before we can feel okay. While this idea may seem noble, it is misguided when it comes to addiction. We must eventually face the truth that we cannot save other people from their own behavior. We can encourage and support their recovery if they ask us to, but even then, we cannot do it for them. When we tell ourselves that we have the power to save someone from their own behavior, it is sometimes called "the illusion of control."

This illusion is pervasive and is often encouraged by popular culture and family upbringing. How many movies about addiction have had the underlying theme that the love of a good woman or man cures addiction? How many testimonials get published quoting people who have recovered from addiction saying that it was a parent's love and tireless effort that pulled them through? How many people were told subtly or overtly that it was up to them to make sure that the other family members were okay? In families where addiction is present in one or both parents, it is easy for the kids to grow up feeling certain that they are responsible for keeping the people around them going. To add confusion, we sometimes hear people who have recovered say that the best thing that happened to them is that their family stopped rescuing them, that "tough love" turned out to work the magic that they needed to recover. Notice, though, that this still encourages family members to think that it is up to them. The reality is that we have little or no control over anyone else.

Sometimes this truth seems hardest for parents of those with addiction. I can't count how many times have I heard, "But I'm a mother (or father)! This is just what parents do. I can't be okay unless I know my kids are okay." You can currently find expensive hand-painted signs to hang in your home that say, "A mother is only as happy as her unhappiest child." You can then find another sign to hang under that one saying, "No one is happy if momma's unhappy." What a setup for the whole family! Through things like this, many of us got family or cultural messages that we are responsible for our children's outcomes. Hormones also play a part in the idea that we must make sure our children are okay no matter the cost to us. That being said, most of us have never stopped to question our underlying assumptions around this when it comes to addiction.

Because it is the nature of addiction to hijack how people make choices, the messages we give ourselves around needing our loved ones to be okay sometimes seem to create more trouble than they solve. This can be seen when we drive ourselves into the ground, when we organize the family around saving the troubled child from themselves, or when we deplete all our energy, time, or money. For all our efforts, things often don't come out the way we want. Our loved one's addiction stays the same, gets worse, or perhaps gets better temporarily then moves back into the familiar destructive patterns. This last can be the hardest, because it suggests that we need to try even harder, that what we have been doing is close but not quite enough.

One of the more helpful ideas is that we can love and support someone without needing them to be okay, especially if that person's choices are what get in the way. The family recovery fellowship Al-Anon calls this "detachment with love." Detachment in this case does not mean pushing loved ones away or kicking them to the curb. It means letting go of the idea that we can control them. It means loving them as they are no matter how bad it seems.

For some of us, it means saying (perhaps only to ourselves), "I will no longer let your actions dictate my emotions." This is easier said than done, but it is possible. It is basically admitting the truth to ourselves and the people we love, then acting accordingly.

I had to learn to do this with my daughter when she went through her teenage years feeling suicidal nearly every day. She went to two junior highs and three high schools during this time, in hopes of finding an environment in which she could prepare for adult life while figuring out how to survive long enough for that to matter. At each school we heard regularly from concerned teachers and administrators that she was sitting in school crying, telling anyone who would listen that she wanted to kill herself. In the first three weeks of freshman year we met or heard from every social worker at the school, the junior parole officer, the head of security, the vice principal, and the principal. All of them told us that we should be concerned. Each had suggestions about how to turn her around, and for the most part they all seemed to care about her, but we were hearing the same things we had been hearing for a while.

In the first few weeks at her last high school, my daughter and I had yet another meeting with a concerned and caring school counselor who told us that their school was not able to handle her, that she needed special help, but who had no real suggestions about where to find it. After all this effort to keep her from ending her own life and accepting that I was powerless to do so, I was finally able to tell her that she would have to make the decision to stay alive or not for herself. I told her that I love her, that if she killed herself I would mourn her for the rest of my life, I would probably look for ways to blame myself like people do, but I could not keep her alive against her will. She was 16 at the time.

Later, I was able to add that I really got that she was suffering, and that if she did kill herself, I would understand. I said that she should avoid doing it because of a temporary chemical imbalance due to medication adjustment, but that I didn't need her to stay alive for me. I said that I would hate it if she died but I would learn to be okay without her if I had to. Although these were scary words to say, I knew it was the right thing and it was the truth. I would need to seek my own serenity rather than demand that she care for herself just so I could feel okay. At the end of the day, this brought more peace to our relationship and demonstrated respect for her as a young adult.

Relief can come for everyone as we let go of the idea that we need to, or ever could, get others to behave. This allows us to see that we can get real work done on ourselves in a way that can always seem frustratingly out of reach when we try to work on anyone else. When family members let go of trying to fix their loved ones, those loved ones often say that they also feel relief. This partly comes because there is less tension in the relationship and less of a sense of scrutiny and criticism. Additionally, most of us do not like to feel like we are being forced to do someone else's will, and yet we may go to great lengths to try to force someone else to do ours when it comes to their recovery.

On a deeper level, many people with addiction say they know their family members want them to get better and that the family feels hurt when this recovery fails to materialize or doesn't stick despite multiple attempts. The person with the addiction thus feels guilt and shame that they can't just switch their addiction off to help their family feel better. If the family starts to get better regardless of whether the person with the addiction is doing so at the same time, the one with addiction can ease their guilt and shame. This allows them to focus on their recovery if and when they are ready.

It was, so to speak, a sobering moment when I saw that my wife would work on herself and learn to be okay without me if she had to. It also set me free to seek my solutions without feeling resentful or guilty and thinking I was doing it for her. We are all ultimately internally motivated, so seeing that my wife was willing to grow with or without me solidified that I wanted a life with her more than I wanted to live in my addiction. This should be a no-brainer, but as we saw in the previous chapter, this really meant that I was willing to give up something that felt vital to my survival in order to live an unknown life that seemed frightening and overwhelming. If I thought I was doing it for her, I could easily fall into resentment towards her for "making" me recover. Instead, she did not insist I do anything. She just made it clear that she would stay with me if I pursued recovery and learn to go on without me if I didn't. We'll look at this more in the section on setting boundaries, but for now all we need to know is that the keystone to her archway of freedom was that she was not going to work on my recovery or push me to do so. She would let me make my own choices and experience the consequences of those choices. She didn't do this to force my hand or teach me a lesson. She just spoke her truth: my recovery was mine alone, and hers would be hers alone as well.

Since that time, we have shared decades in recovery together. We tell each other how we are doing, what recovery steps we are working on, where we struggle. Through all of it, however, we are clear that we each have our own work to do. We aren't perfect about this, of course. We sometimes give unsolicited feedback, try to influence each other's recovery in the direction we would like, and certainly each have opinions of how the other is doing. When these moments come, we can reorient ourselves with the simple reminder that each of us is responsible for our own growth. If we catch ourselves crossing the line, we can use the recovery principle of making amends as soon as we see that we were in the wrong. We can admit that we were speaking out of fear or selfishness and remind ourselves that our fears are not facts. We can seek support from others in our recovery fellowships, and sometimes talking to our mentors about things that are too challenging to bring up with our partners at that time. While my wife and I go to some meetings together, we make sure we each also have meetings that we attend by ourselves. When we go to meetings together, we keep a rule that neither of us comments on what the other shared in the meeting.

All of this allows us to have a wonderful life together and gain the things I wish for you and your family: health, happiness, and a shared language of recovery.

Cascading Recovery

My family's story illustrates that recovery can cascade through families, sometimes quickly, sometimes slowly. Ours is only one of the many cases I have seen where one person in the family gets into recovery, then later another family member tries it out, and then yet another family member gets involved in their own recovery. There is no predictable timeline for this, and your mileage may vary as to which or how many family members recover. One friend of mine says they worked on their recovery for 12 years while waiting for their spouse to get on board. Now they attend meetings both together and separately, and they have become one of my favorite couples.

There is nothing more positive for your addicted family member than having you and other family members embrace their own recovery. This does not mean that it is your job to corral your family members into recovery. Even if you could get everyone to start working on themselves, there is no guarantee that the addicted person would suddenly see the light. Instead, it means that you may be the recovery pioneer in your family and lead by example rather than by trying to get others to do what you think they should do. You have seen how much one person with addiction can affect the rest of the family. It stands to reason that one person in recovery can have a similarly powerful impact, but in a much more positive way. That person could be you.

While there is no guarantee that working on your recovery will lead to your addicted loved one doing the same, I can say with confidence that it will improve the atmosphere in your home, leave you less stressed, and open the door to many other positive things that you may have assumed could only happen if your loved one got and stayed sober. These could include a greater sense of wellbeing, improved sleep, less daily stress, letting go of obsession, increased satisfaction in work and other daily activities, and improved outlook on life.

The cascade of recovery can go beyond your family. As you work on your recovery, you will likely find that others around you are dealing with similar issues. Friends, coworkers, and people in your volunteer group or place of worship will know the pain you have felt in seeing a loved one struggle with addiction, because some of them have felt it, too. Some will have sought their own recovery while others may not have considered this as a possibility. Many will feel alone, and you can help ease their sense of isolation and helplessness. In families where addiction has been a burden for generations, there may be great reluctance to discuss such matters outside of the family, but people often feel comfortable enough to open up if they know they are talking with others who have gone through the same things.

This will be helpful for you, too, especially if the people in your family don't seem to be "getting it" as fast as you would like, or perhaps at all. Knowing that you can help someone who really wants that help can be some reassurance for all involved. It is much more productive than trying to force solutions on those who are not ready yet. For those of us who have trouble sitting still or standing by while our loved ones struggle, having this healthier outlet for our energy can be an amazing blessing.

If working on your recovery while your loved one is still suffering sounds selfish to you, let me reassure you that the time you spend working on yourself is never wasted, and it will benefit anyone with whom you come into contact. Once I realized that my recovery was helping the people around me regardless of whether they were working on their recovery, it began to seem like an act of selfishness to *not* work on my recovery.

There are those who say that recovery *should* be selfish. I know they mean well in encouraging people to recover for themselves and be undeterred by naysayers, but I disagree that anything about recovery is selfish. Selfishness means not caring who gets hurt when I get my way. My recovery has instead been a gift I can give to anyone with whom I can come into contact, and it is a constant motivation to be of service to others. This is a kind of win-win deal that is rarely offered in life.

Thus, I found motivation to go to meetings when I would rather have gone out to dinner, to dig deeper into my issues in therapy when it might have seemed easier to let sleeping dogs lie, to talk to others about my struggles when I might have rather maintained an image, or to sit in morning meditation when hitting the snooze button seemed like bliss. I knew that anything I did for myself would ultimately be good for the whole family.

Recovery can be done through recovery fellowships (more on these later), individual and group therapy, family workshops, spiritual counseling through a place of worship, and in personal work such as meditation and contemplation.

You can use and all of these, and they often build on each other.

Don't Try This Alone

Addiction is too large a problem for anyone to tackle on their own. I never recommend anyone who is trying to get sober go it alone. This goes just as much for families as the people with addiction. There is an abundance of support available for families, much of it free, but so many do not know it is there for them or they feel resistant to accepting it.

Some families find their own way to get through all the issues that come with loving someone who has an addiction. However, when I talk to them, they show more pain, anger, and sadness than those who find support in their journey. This is admittedly a non-scientific sample, but there is relatively little research on families of those with addiction, and even less on those who try to tackle it on their own. What I can say with certainty is that I see great relief come to those who seek help in addressing these issues after trying on their own for years. I'm going to assume that if you could have solved your family's issues with addiction by yourself, you would have done it already and wouldn't be reading this book. Let me assure you that there is no shame in this. I certainly couldn't do it on my own, and I tried for most of my life.

With my father, I thought up every scheme to try to control or stop his drinking. I daydreamed about pouring all the alcohol out or putting something noxious in the bottles, but I knew this might be suicide, so I was never brave enough to try. Instead, I cycled through being nice, funny, angry, rebellious, challenging, resentful, and silent in turns. I tried to entertain him while he was drunk, or I tried to engage him in conversation. I got him another drink when he asked, even though I didn't want him to drink it. I made up answers to his drunken questions. I tried to get him to feel guilty the next morning. I know I wasn't the only one trying, because I watched the energy of the entire family change when he began drinking as we all tried to avoid or manage him. Not surprisingly, nothing made any difference, but that never slowed our efforts. It didn't occur to me that there was help available. In fact, talking about the drinking was strongly discouraged within the family, and when I told anyone outside of the family, I got lectured if word of this reached home. Therefore, I decided to hold it in and not ask for help. I already tended to try to do things on my own, so this only reinforced my general life pattern.

When I later saw compulsive behavior in my wife and myself, I had learned to turn a blind eye to addiction so well that I thought we couldn't be addicted. There were times when I enabled her addiction so that she would enable mine. At other times that I tried to control her behavior, and I used many of the same strategies that had failed so miserably with my dad. They didn't do any better with my wife. I never thought to ask anyone else if they knew what to do. It was finally my own addiction that made me desperate and humble enough to seek recovery. It was amazing to see that I had to get so miserable before I was ready to accept help, only to discover that there had been an almost infinite supply of guidance and relief available all along.

Where is this help? It can come in many forms. Often, the help available for families is analogous to the things that most help people with addiction. This includes recovery fellowships, spirituality, and counseling. We will look at each of these in detail.

One of the most important factors in addiction recovery is the sense of connection found in groups of people who are dealing with the same issues.

While this idea did not start with Alcoholics Anonymous [AA], that group has proven to be the most successful in terms of both longevity and the number of people helped[4], so their approach will be used as an example. According to the first members of that fellowship, they were as amazed as anyone else that their approach worked, but many grabbed onto it with all they had and passed it along to others who struggled with alcohol.[5] While these AA members were busy trying to establish a method with which they could help themselves and others to conquer their compulsive alcohol use, some of their spouses were doing their best to be supportive and involved. In the course of this, something even more unexpected happened: the spouses found that they were benefitting just as much from getting together with each other as the first AA members were.[6] Over time, they formed their own groups and used AA's Twelve Steps for their own personal growth, finding they could have peace and even happiness whether the person with the drinking problem got better or not.[6] They named their group "Al-Anon" and it is still going strong. Today, there are a number of other recovery fellowships either specifically for families or open to them, including Families Anonymous, Nar-Anon, SMART Recovery Family & Friends, and Celebrate Recovery.

These fellowships are usually run by and for friends and family of people with addiction, people like yourself who are more than willing to pass along what they have learned about how to be okay in the face of such a difficult illness. Most recovery fellowships are free to all who need them.

There is likely at least one meeting near you, and they can be most easily found through an Internet search or by calling a local outreach number. If there is no local meeting, or the local ones don't feel like a good fit, there are phone meetings, video meetings, and groups on social media. As our society develops new ways to communicate and connect, someone will probably find a way to use them to spread the message of recovery.

Here's what you can expect when you go to a meeting. First off, most meetings are based in the Twelve Steps and tend to take place at local churches, not for any religious reason, but simply because churches tend to have meeting rooms that are easy and inexpensive to rent. These fellowships are based in anonymity, so everyone typically only uses their first name and optionally their last initial. Along the same lines, people hold what is said and who they see at meetings in confidence. This is usually announced at least once during the meeting. These traditions in the groups create a sense of safety for those who are nervous about being seen at a meeting, let alone sharing openly about family problems. Many people who have addiction in their family history have been raised in a family culture that forbids speaking openly about the addiction, and those who have active addiction in the family often feel shame about what is happening in their homes, so this atmosphere of safety is vital.

Most meetings start with readings from a scripted format. Twelve Step fellowships such as Al-Anon often start with the Serenity Prayer. Beginning with a set prayer is a tradition that may bring a sense of familiarity and comfort to some who are new to the program, while seeming overly religious to others. You are not required to participate in the prayer and no one should comment if you do or don't. While the prayer starts with the word "God," those who are not inclined toward monotheistic religion may see it as a general spiritual offering or simply a reminder that people are gathered to find what they can and can't change in their lives and the lives of those they love. There may be several readings, including a special reading if anyone is at their first meeting. If this makes you self-conscious, don't worry. Everyone there had a first meeting once.

After the readings are completed, the leader of the meeting (a position that regularly rotates) may offer a topic or read from fellowship literature. The meeting then opens up for sharing. Most people state their first name when they want to share, the group greets them by name, and then the person shares. For instance, if I was at such a meeting, I would open my sharing by saying, "My name is Casey." Group members might respond, "Hi, Casey." Then I would talk about whatever was on my heart or mind. When I was done, I might say, "Thank you," and group members might respond by saying, "Thanks, Casey."

One person talks at a time and the rest listen quietly. Others do not comment specifically on what someone else shared, offer feedback, give advice, or engage in side conversations (all of this is known as "crosstalk"). This respectful environment is a great benefit by itself since some group members are coming from families in which people talk or shout over each other, in which unsolicited opinions and feedback are the norm, and in which some family members do not feel safe to make their viewpoint or feelings known for fear of conflict and criticism.

When the time of sharing is done, usually a few minutes before the scheduled closing time for the meeting, there may be a final reading or statement and then the group closes. In Twelve Step groups, there may be another brief prayer, such as another recitation of the Serenity Prayer. After this, there is a time when people mill around, talk to each other, and exchange contact information. Some people refer to this as "the meeting after the meeting," and might later say that this was the part that made the biggest difference for them that day. They might hear something they really needed to hear or say something they really needed to say during this time of informal fellowship.

You may note that Twelve Step groups often open and close with prayer. This is because these groups stress a spiritual solution even though they are not religiously affiliated.[7] By spirituality, the groups mean that members have found relief by leaning on a power greater than themselves and then doing personal work to connect more with that power. Such a higher power could be a religious god or gods, nature, the universe, the spirit of the recovery group, the idea of your highest self, science, or anything else greater than you to which you can feel connection and from which you derive benefit.[8] Because no one in the group can say what another person's higher power should be and there is no obligation to ever tell anyone else what you have chosen, strict atheists and deeply religious people sit side by side in these fellowships and find recovery through a common solution.

Brain research has shown that spirituality provides a key for people to move out of reactive fear and into rational thought, thereby able to make decisions that benefit their future.[9] This idea may provide a scientific explanation for why spirituality has been a lynchpin in so many successful recovery groups, and why Twelve Step fellowships and other spiritual support groups inspired by their model work for so many people not only around addiction, but also with other mental and emotional issues.[10] The form of the spirituality doesn't affect the quality of recovery[8], the words said in prayer and meditation don't determine the sense of serenity[9], the choice of which higher power a person seeks doesn't predict who recovers and who doesn't.[8] Instead, the quality of serenity and recovery seems to come from the feeling of connection to something greater than ourselves that can guide us, regardless of what higher power is chosen for this role. As a deeply religious friend once said with a wry smile, "I still believe that to get into Heaven, Jesus is necessary, but to recover from addiction, a doorknob will do." While I have never met anyone who actually used a doorknob as their higher power, the phrase "you can even use a doorknob" is often used as an example of how open-minded Twelve Step recovery members are when it comes to spirituality.

Spirituality is not necessary for recovery, however. Fellowships such as SMART Recovery and Rational Recovery were formed as alternatives to the spiritual approach. The founder of Rational Recovery says he liked that Alcoholics Anonymous exists for those who find it effective, but felt that spirituality was not for him and wanted to make sure that there was an effective alternative available. [11] Instead of relying on spiritual solutions, some of these fellowships seek to use proven therapeutic techniques, such as Rational Emotive Behavioral Therapy [REBT]. These fellowships see eye-to-eye with Twelve Step recovery groups on one thing: that a winning strategy to overcome addiction is to gather together with others who are working on themselves to beat the same problem.

Another popular strategy is to seek counseling for the individual and/or the family to recover from the effects of addiction. Many of my private practice clients have come in saying they don't feel comfortable going to groups but feel they can talk to someone one-on-one. I understand this perspective and am happy to work with them on this basis, but I also strongly encourage them to explore one or more of the recovery fellowships anyway. Some do and some don't, but I would be remiss if I didn't point out that there is free help all around them. This is partly because I think everyone should know their options before laying down hard-earned money for counseling, but also because they may need help long after they have ended their counseling sessions, and I want them to know that it is always available wherever they are. Some who have stated in their first session that I had better not send them to "those meetings" have nonetheless agreed to try a few, and have come back with glowing reviews and determination to stick with those fellowships. Others never seem to connect or find what they need in recovery groups. Even then, I know that they have at least tried everything available to them and may find years later that one fellowship or another is better than struggling on their own.

Can recovery be done alone? For some people it can, for others it seems impossible. One of the largest long-term surveys ever taken showed that most people never get any help for addiction, yet the majority of them recover anyway.[12] A good bit of this seems to be attributable to the "ageing-out" of drug abuse that happens for many people as their brain finishes maturing in their mid-20's while they concurrently are facing more of life's responsibilities. Some might contend that such people were never truly addicted, but this argument tempts circular definitions.

What seems safer to say is that like any disease, some people have a worse case of addiction than others, and so recovery will naturally be easier for some people. Many may be able to beat it without help because they have fewer of the genetic, psychological, and/or environmental risk factors[12], and some will have more of the protective factors as well. For all the people who quit abusing drugs or addictive behaviors on their own, however, there are many who do not seem to be able to do so without help, no matter the strength of their resolve and how hard they try. Others find that even if they could quit on their own, it is easier and more rewarding to do it in community with others.

My father, who drank alcohol compulsively for most of his life, quit in the last two years of his life without help. When I asked my mother how it was for him, she said he was miserable. This seems to be in part because he isolated himself from all his old drinking friends without replacing them with new connections. Additionally, he does not seem to have dealt with the emotional issues that fueled his drinking in the first place. Instead, he just gave up his go-to coping mechanism and suffered without it. My heart grieves that he didn't allow himself to get the support that I had on the difficult journey of recovery. He certainly knew it was available; he used to drive a friend to AA meetings but not go for himself. We never got a chance to discuss any of this because we were barely talking at the time he got sober, and then shortly after I got into recovery, he died of complications from his long-term addiction to cigarettes.

People who research addiction usually agree that getting help, whether professional or through recovery fellowships, makes things easier, and that many people need more help than they are offered or are willing to accept. This seems likely to be even more true for family members since so many of them don't know how much help is available, let alone think they need it. Most people come to a family workshop with the sole goal of helping their loved one, not having considered their own needs in this difficult time. This is no surprise given the messages that so many of us get from family culture, society, and the media.

Family cultural patterns around addiction may include things such as stewing in anger at the person with addiction, staying silent or helpless about the pain addiction is causing everyone, denying anything is wrong, taking on a sense of responsibility to put everyone else's needs first, or variations on these things that lead everyone around the person with addiction to suffer. These things may be directly taught or absorbed through watching other family members' examples. Family members are too rarely encouraged to speak up for their own needs or to make sure they are okay before trying to help anyone else.

Society can give similar messages. Family members may be lauded as courageous and strong for ignoring their own wellbeing in order to do "anything it takes" to save the person with addiction. People are encouraged to be selfless without regard for the cost. Sometimes our society pushes families to stay isolated in the face of their pain because no one around them knows what to do with it. Families may find awkward silences rather than support if they talk to those who do not understand. Some people they approach may have their own family culture of secrecy and helplessness about addiction or may offer well-intentioned advice that is not based in any practical experience.

In the media, addiction is splashed across news sites, celebrity profiles, and in all sorts of fiction. In these stories we see people in and out of recovery, and we celebrate the testimony of those who overcome their disease. Family members are mostly left out of these stories, however. When they are included, they are sometimes demonized, and other times portrayed as heartbroken victims or selfless supporters. How often, though, do we see accounts of how the family members got help for themselves, found their own recovery, and grew through the experience of loving someone with an addiction? No wonder family members rarely think in terms of their own recovery.

Luckily, there are hundreds of thousands of family members who do seek recovery and share it freely with others.[13] The vast majority of those who participated in Al-Anon's latest survey say their lives have improved in terms of overall wellbeing, mental health, emotional state, and spiritual connection.[13] I urge you to find and engage with such people.

The Power of Loving Honesty

Honesty is a core human value[14], the one that I most often hear families request from their addicted loved ones, and the one that seems hardest to deliver. Even though most people know this, many still take it personally when their addicted loved one is dishonest. To make matters worse, family members may see where an addicted loved one struggles in this area but miss where the family can fall into dishonesty as well, no matter how well-intentioned. Finally, those family members who manage to stay honest while dealing with addiction may do so in ways that are not loving.

It is not hard to see the cause of so much dishonesty on the part of people with addiction. The disease causes many behavioral changes that center in the subconscious survival mechanisms of the brain, as outlined in Chapter One. Human history has illustrated all too well that when survival is on the line, people will do all sorts of things that they would otherwise never do. This certainly includes becoming dishonest, whether only in specific situations and areas of life, or as a habit in all relationships. For some people, the dishonesty of addiction may be a break with their lifelong character, something they despair at doing yet which seems compulsively necessary in order to use or act out one more time. For others, it is an extension of the dishonesty and manipulation they used as childhood coping skills. Deception and denial may bring the person a sense of control or safety despite knowing on some level that it is not who they would rather be. In such a case, the existing dishonesty is strongly reinforced by the perceived need to keep the addiction going at all costs.

Regardless of how this dishonesty feels to the person with the addiction, it is usually hurtful for those closest to them. This is natural, given the importance of honesty to not only build trust but also as a basic means of creating satisfaction and reducing negativity in relationships.[15] Nonetheless, when it comes to dealing with addiction, taking it personally is a mistake because there is little sense or profit in taking a brain disease personally. Hopefully, we wouldn't take the symptoms of someone's asthma as a sign they don't love us, or the symptoms of a person's bipolar disorder as proof that we have failed somehow. Similarly, when we recognize that dishonesty is a natural and common symptom of addiction[16], then we don't need to think of it as a reflection of the quality of our relationship or love. The dishonesty of someone with an active addiction is no more a gauge of their love and respect than are the voices heard by someone with schizophrenia or the variable blood sugar levels of someone with diabetes.

In my case, I was routinely dishonest for two major reasons as a child: the first was that I feared I was not good enough to keep around as I was, and the second was that when growing up with a dad who drank addictively, it was clearly not safe to speak certain truths. I thus engaged in constant fabrication and obscuring of the truth because I thought it was my best bet for survival. Thus, I was thinking both like someone with active addiction and like a family member of someone with active addiction since before I can remember. If I had a normal brain, I might have outgrown all this. Instead, around age 10, I consciously decided that the addictive lifestyle was for me, and my dishonesty only increased. I became more sophisticated in my deceptions and used them to hide and justify my addictive acting out, while also learning to present whatever I thought people wanted to see. As I grew older, this became a fundamental part of my existence. No one knew the complete truth about my acting out or my opinions and I would have denied these at all costs because I lived in terror of being found out. The more my addiction grew, the more I developed two lives lived in the same body, one of which I compulsively hid from the world.

My dishonesty was not personal to anyone. I was not lying or hiding because I didn't love or respect those around me. No one raised me to be dishonest, I knew it wasn't what I was supposed to do, and I knew it was upsetting to my family. I wanted to make them happy, but I was convinced that I couldn't be honest and survive. There are few motivators stronger than our survival instinct, so I kept giving in to the impulse to be dishonest, which became both habit and imperative over time. I'm sure my family took it personally, and I can't blame them, but this did no good to anyone and it certainly didn't change my behavior.

It was not until several years into my recovery that I would see that I had been highly valued all along. It took a lot of therapy and recovery work to recognize that even though I had long since moved out of my parents' home, I was still living by the old "house rules" I had made up, such as staying mostly silent about emotional matters and being dishonest about anything that I thought would make me too vulnerable. I would sometimes trot out sordid details of my past or my family history in order to garner sympathy or attention but avoided any parts that brought on shame or fear.

When I finally started my journey of sobriety, the spirituality of my recovery program strongly encouraged me to live by my highest principles and gave me confidence that I would be okay if I did. This gradually made it easier to follow the internal moral compass that I never knew I had and thus to strive for honesty with all people.

If you can begin to let go of personalizing the symptoms of addiction, you may see that your own recovery moves you in the direction of greater honesty as well. Some family members will say that honesty has never been a problem for them but nonetheless ask me what they should say to their loved one to keep them sober. They tell me that they walk on eggshells or suppress their feelings out of fear that they will trigger a blowup or even a relapse. Family members routinely avoid saying what is on their hearts and pretend to be okay when they are not, such as telling friends and neighbors that everyone in the family is just fine. No matter how well intentioned, these things are all fundamentally dishonest.

Many family members are selectively dishonest so routinely that they don't even realize they are doing it, let alone why. If they explore their actions and motivations, they almost invariably find they are reacting to fear. They most often fear that being truthful will cause their loved one to spin out of control and that this will thus be the family member's fault. Sometimes the person with the addiction will encourage this fallacy, such as by saying, "You make me so mad/hurt/sad that I have to drink." Perhaps these words are never said out loud, but instead a pattern is established in which the family tries to be honest and then the addicted person acts out. Over time, the family learns to avoid being honest in any way that seems upsetting to the addicted one.

To exacerbate this problem, some family members grew up in families where addiction was part of the family history and culture, so emotional dishonesty was modeled and even encouraged. Some were told as children to stay quiet about family business, perhaps hearing, "We don't air our dirty laundry in the street," or, "Don't ever tell anyone what goes on in this house." They may have grown up learning to "go along to get along." Perhaps they picked up a pattern of avoiding conflict wherever possible. Some gave up on speaking their truth because it seemed to make no difference, or even worked against them.

A woman in one of my workshops once said that as a girl she was told that if she was crying, she should go in the bathroom and not come out until she had cleaned up and could put a smile on her face. In telling us this, she realized that she had taken this as a powerful lesson that she should hide her true emotions and only present what others found pleasing. This carried into all her relationships but was especially present when she avoided expressing emotions that her addicted loved one didn't seem to like. This is an illustration of how family members can find themselves moving further and further from their core value of honesty, and not even realize it is happening.

Recovery can move you back into alignment with your honesty. This may happen through letting go of the fear that your honesty will be the undoing of your loved one's sobriety. It may come through trust that a higher power will lead you to the best expression of your truth. It may come through seeing other members of a recovery fellowship be open and honest in ways that you have been scared to try or may not even have considered. Perhaps you will see that holding back has not gotten you what you wanted anyway. A program of recovery will tend to push you towards any and all of these things by connecting you with others who have tried the way of honesty and found it freeing. Fellowships will encourage you to explore what blocks your honesty, and in the case of Twelve Step groups, will encourage you to connect with a higher power that can sustain and support you in this journey.

What about those of us who consider ourselves honest to a fault, or perhaps would say we are brutally honest? In this case, the problem is not honesty but the style in which it is given. More of this will be covered later in this book in the section on communication style and boundaries, but we can say for now that an honest message can always be delivered with love and compassion. When honesty is given with harshness, it is often an attempt to change someone else's behavior or attitude. In other words, it is manipulation. Manipulation is inherently dishonest, even if it is done in the name of "only speaking the truth." Some of this may come through being selective about what is shared. For instance, when someone says they are brutally honest, they usually mean they are very honest about others' behaviors, faults, etc. People rarely mean that they are brutally honest about their own more tender feelings and vulnerabilities. For such people, it can be a challenge to see past saying things they think will "work" and instead express what is truly on their heart, such as love, fear, sadness, and hope. They often find themselves speaking only from anger or judgment.

All of this may be best summed up with a quote from Warren Wiersbe: "Truth without love is brutality, and love without truth is hypocrisy."[17] This suggests that in speaking our truth without compassion, we will likely do more harm than good, whereas trying to be loving without speaking that truth is really another form of dishonesty. Both approaches may be motivated by the best intentions, but both tend to stem from a desire to shape or control someone else's behavior and experience. This is not only futile; it will probably push us further from the connection and love we wanted in the first place.

We Don't Need Your Identification

One way in which families with addiction often organize themselves is to take on the Identified Patient model. In this way of thinking, the person with the addiction is the Identified Patient [IP] and other family members become focused on that person, often blaming any family problems on the IP and their issues.[18] This idea is so pervasive that the person with the addiction often subscribes to it, blaming themselves for everything wrong in the family. The IP model might be best summarized in the idea that "We'd all be fine if (insert IP's name here) would get it together."

In my professional experience, this is never true, but I certainly bought into it as I was growing up. I thought that I was the source of the family's problems most of the time, and there were undoubtedly times when other family members agreed. I believed that if I could just do better, get better grades, act right, etc., then the rest of the family would be okay. Maybe that would be enough to get my dad to stop drinking or exploding in anger. Maybe my mom would become a happy person. Maybe my brother and I would get along better. This all felt very frustrating because I felt powerless to make these changes, or at least to sustain them for any period of time. No matter how good my intentions, I found myself compelled to go back to my destructive and troubling behaviors, sometimes feeling like a helpless bystander watching myself screw everything up one more time. I would see the look on my family's faces and assume they all agreed that I was the problem in my family. This was reinforced by my family's efforts, however well-intentioned, to get me to change. There were many different schemes to turn my behavior around, some more focused on punishment and shaming, others based on enticing rewards. None made enough of a difference to justify all the effort, but this reinforced the idea that my problems were *the* family problem, to the point that I was often blind to the struggles my other family members had.

Sometimes, the family may see different family members as the IP at different times, or there may be disagreement about who is who. For instance, I sometimes saw my father as the IP because of his alcohol use. I had a dream of getting him to stop drinking, although I quickly learned that this could never be spoken out loud. Instead, I came up with futile plots to change his mood and behavior. At the same time, my father seemed to see me as the IP, like a project that he had taken on when I was adopted. This is not to discount his love for me, but the IP dynamic was there from the beginning. He tried all sorts of things to deal with my antisocial and at times confusing or contradictory behaviors, while I was trying just as hard to come up with some way to change his drinking. As we will see in the later section on family roles, my behavioral struggles served an important, although completely unconscious, function in the family: they gave all of us somewhere to put our focus besides my dad's drinking. Unfortunately, this not only preserved family dysfunction, but it also left any issues my brother and mother had overshadowed by whatever dust my dad or I were kicking up. I suspect my brother's successes were similarly overshadowed at times since my parents had to focus attention on my issues instead.

My story shows how the IP model of thinking can lead families to scapegoating the IP, as well as trying to fix or save the IP, when in fact the whole family needs help. With this dynamic in play, everyone suffers in some way. The one with addiction usually falls into shame that only puts them at greater risk of relapse, while the family sits in anger, fear, guilt, or shame. If the family remains stuck in this dynamic, they miss out on an opportunity to grow together, and often start to grow apart.

Many families, including mine growing up, appear to be high-functioning by social standards, such as working productively, living in an affluent area, earning the respect of their community, etc. When we start to explore underlying feelings and beliefs, however, there usually turns out to be distress, and we often find that some of it is older than the current addiction. That is to say, addiction can bring out buried family issues just as much as it can create new ones. If there are ways in which the family does not communicate well, for instance, these will be highlighted by communication breakdowns when addiction adds additional stress to the family system. While it may be tempting to blame this solely on the IP, the faulty communication pattern was probably in place from the beginning. Addiction just showed us where it could use improvement.

If this can be recognized and embraced, the family stands to benefit from all it has been through, turning addiction from a curse into what one of my early mentors called "a weirdly wrapped gift." By this, she meant that when the family gets on the road of realistic hope, they have opportunities to heal and grow in ways that they may never have done under any other circumstances.

The rest of this book will focus on just how this can be accomplished.

Chapter 3

The Ins and Outs of Recovery

There is a recovery path for everyone who wants it. Some may never think they need it, but I haven't seen anyone who could not benefit from trying some of the many options available, whether they have the addiction or are in a loving relationship with someone else who does. This chapter will explore some of the ways recovery can show up, including examining how change happens and what recovery and relapse look like both for the person with addiction and those who love them.

Stages of Change

Family members often lament that their addicted loved one doesn't seem to want to change or can't make change stick, yet the same family members may overlook similar patterns in their own thinking and behavior. It turns out that some patterns around change are common to people everywhere. In fact, two researchers in the early 1980's proposed a model for how people change that has enjoyed popularity ever since: the Stages of Change model.[1] They were studying how people quit smoking cigarettes, but their model has been generalized not only to other drugs (yes, smoking is drug use) but also to how individuals, organizations, and even societies deal with change. The model includes five stages with an optional sixth stage:

1. Precontemplation
2. Contemplation
3. Preparation
4. Action
5. Maintenance
6. Relapse (optional)

Each of these stages applies for both the person with addiction and their families, but the stages are not a smooth, linear progression. Instead, people often find themselves jumping around the stages, and they may be at different stages for different problems or even aspects of a problem. Certainly, various members of the family may be in different stages from each other at any given time. Understanding this to be true, let's look at each stage in detail and see how it may apply to your own experience.

Precontemplation

Precontemplation is the stage in which you don't think you have a problem. Any issues that arise get blamed on other people or outside forces. For instance, if I notice my jeans are getting tighter, I think, "It must be the dryer." For the person with the addiction, this can be a very long stage. They don't want to see their using as a problem, therefore anything that goes wrong as a result of using is quickly blamed on someone or something else. Remember in my personal story when I said I didn't think my wife and I were addicted, instead thinking we were just cooler than everyone else? That's Precontemplation. As many people have experienced, family members make convenient scapegoats in this stage. "If you treated me differently, I wouldn't drink like this." "You raised me wrong and that's why I use." "You need to change, not me." "Why do you keep hounding me about smoking pot when dad drinks?" "If you would just leave me alone, I'd be fine." Family can find themselves defending their actions, getting increasingly angry, or throwing up their hands in frustration at these accusations. Some may realize that when they get caught up in these discussions, it seems like no progress is made and they end up talking about everything except how their loved one will get better. Having a loved one in Precontemplation can seem like an endlessly frustrating experience.

Family members can sit in Precontemplation as well. They may refuse to see that their loved one has a problem. "Not my child." "That's what all college kids do." "It can't be that bad." "She's making a good living, so she's entitled to blow off some steam." "He's from (insert ethnic group here). They all drink like that." Family members can also be in Precontemplation about their own need for recovery from the effects of someone else's addiction. "Why do I need to change? I'm not the one with a problem." "If they would just be okay, I could be okay." "We'd be fine if they would just shape up." What can be most difficult is when one or more family members are in Precontemplation around their own compulsive behavior. I once had a parent in family workshop who mentioned that they had gambled away a large sum of money compulsively on the way to the workshop. While they berated themselves for doing this and admitted that once they started gambling it was difficult for them to stop, they still professed that they could not relate to their child's struggle with alcohol. After all, they explained, drinking had never been a problem for them. Sometimes, family members can even be compulsively using the same drug as their loved one yet fail to see the commonality. They may say that they "know how to handle it" since their lives are currently looking better than the family member in treatment. This can lead to deep resentments and conflict in the family, all because it is much easier to see the painful truth of someone else's behavior than our own.

In my own life, I've been on both sides of the coin. In active addiction, I would deny to myself that I had a problem. Driving under the influence to end up in the arms of someone other than my wife? No problem. "It was a one-time thing." Continuous emotional affairs with strong sexual overtones? No problem. "I get along better with women and gay or bisexual men." Eating an entire tray of cookies in one sitting? No problem. "I just really like those cookies." Taking out a home equity line of credit then running it up so high that I was making payments on the line of credit with money from the same line of credit? No problem. "Something always works itself out." Spending the day smoking pot when I was supposed to be at a family function? No problem. "We're the cool, rebellious ones." I just did what I wanted, and since it's what I wanted, I decided it was no problem. That's Precontemplation.

I also had no problem seeing my family members' problems. When my daughter was performing below what I thought was her potential in third grade, I was ready to spring into action. I thought another lecture might do the trick, or perhaps another consequence was just what the doctor ordered. If you had asked me, I would have said that my daughter's behavior made me disappointed and angry. I was deep in Precontemplation about how little control I actually had over her and how little she had to do with my emotional distress. Even though I could see that my behavior wasn't getting her to do what I wanted, I kept trying the same things over and over again, expecting different results. I hadn't considered that I was working myself up over her choices. She didn't cause me to do that. I was making my own barely-considered choices to engage from a place of expectation and resentment. I knew I didn't want to be that way, but I hadn't thought enough about my part in things. This is what kept me stuck in Precontemplation.

Contemplation

When a situation becomes painful enough, however, we can start to move into the next stage: Contemplation. In this stage, we start to think that maybe the problem is our actions and attitudes rather than other people or outside forces. In the case of the tightening jeans, I might think, "Maybe it's the donuts and not the dryer." Notice that I only say "maybe" because in this stage we are thinking about the problem in a new way but we aren't doing anything about it yet. This may be the first time we consider our role in the issue as being anything besides the victim or innocent bystander. We haven't made any big decisions, let alone changed anything in our behavior, but this is definitely progress.

For me, this looked like considering for the first time that I wasn't a hopeless sicko, something I had secretly thought for decades, but that I was someone with a problem called addiction, and there was a well-established solution. This was a huge paradigm shift. It put the problem in my lap rather than making it everyone else's fault. I was no longer smarter, faster, and better than everyone else, and therefore above their petty standards. I was a guy who had some work to do on himself. I wasn't sure what that work would entail, and it would be years before I committed to it enough to establish lasting sobriety, but at least I was thinking about it.

When someone with addiction starts considering their part in the problem, it can be encouraging for the family. Some may even think that this must be the turning point they have been waiting for all this time. "She's finally seeing her problem. Things will get better from here." Family members may feel a flood of emotions as their loved one talks about their newfound insight. This may include relief, joy, or even pent-up sadness, but it may just as easily show up as anger. "It's about time!" "I've been saying this for years." "Why did she listen to some stranger at a meeting when she wouldn't listen to me? They are just telling her the same thing I've been saying all along." Family may be tempted to try to drive the point home, perhaps out of fear that the insight they are hearing will slip away. They might make recovery the only subject of conversation or give example after example of how they have been hurt or how hopeful they are for the future now that the problem is on the table. None of this is likely to help.

You can bypass some of these dead-end detours by getting into Contemplation yourself. This may look like facing your loved one's problems squarely and honestly or it may look like facing your own issues. It will be most profitable to start accepting the fact that you have no control over someone else's thinking, attitude, and actions. As Al-Anon says, you didn't cause it, you can't cure it, and you can't control it (many call this "The Three C's"). The Contemplation stage involves considering that these ideas may be true. It doesn't mean making them part of your life right away. It does mean being willing to not only consider a new conception of your loved one's problem, but also to find and reduce any internal resistance you may have to that new conception.

It is this internal resistance that is most likely to put you back into Precontemplation. For instance, some of us are used to being the fixer or rescuer of the family. We may have been raised with messages that it is our responsibility to make sure everyone else is okay. This can be especially true if there is addiction in past and present generations. If this is the case, then we will likely struggle with the idea that we don't have practical influence over whether or not someone else acts out in their addiction. We may find ourselves continually returning to the idea that if we just tried harder, yelled louder, acted nicer, or use more of whatever strategy we cling to, we could finally make the vital difference.

We are often really struggling with our emotional reaction to seeing someone we love in active addiction or early recovery. In seeking to escape our own discomfort, we can return to Precontemplation, in which we blame the addiction and/or the person who has it for our discomfort. In fact, it is our internal sense of responsibility that is causing us to feel as much pain as we do. It can also be scary to challenge long-held beliefs about our role in others' lives, so it is easy to return to Precontemplation, and start telling ourselves that we should try one more time to control someone else's addictive behavior. If we can push through this and stick with our Contemplation anyway, we find that we are ready to move into the next stage.

Preparation

This would put us into Preparation. This is the stage where we start to think about what we will do differently to get away from the discomfort our current behavior has been bringing. In the example of the tightening jeans, I now think, "I'm going to find a gym and start jogging every morning. It's salads for lunch from now on." I may also start telling those around me about the positive changes I am planning. For the person with addiction, this may sound like, "I won't quit altogether, but I'm going to cut down on how much I drink," or, "I'm ready to go to AA," or even, "I'm done for good. Can you help me find a treatment center?" When we hear such things, we know that the person with addiction has hit a new stage in their recovery. This can be celebrated for the milestone that it is, but keep in mind that nothing has actually changed at this stage. As an old riddle goes: Three frogs sit on a log and two decide to jump off. How many frogs are left on the log?

Three, because they only *decided* to jump.

In my addiction, Preparation looked like three weeks of reading about sex addiction and thinking that I might need find a local meeting, but not picking up the phone to find one. During this time, my addictive behavior worsened. Perhaps I was scared to think that I would really be changing and so I subconsciously wanted to get in as much acting out as I could. Perhaps I was trying to convince myself to get off the fence and either give in more fully to my addiction or finally get help. Whatever the deeper motivation, I was horrified to see myself get worse just when I was considering getting better. It was this sense of internal conflict that inspired my wife to ask what was going on, and which motivated me to finally tell her everything.

It may be illustrative to see that while I started into the Action stage by attending meetings, I was still in Preparation about doing what the people at those meetings did to stay sober. I would read the basic text of the fellowship and tried some of what they said to do, but I put off the biggest actions and ideas for years.

During this time, I had a number of "slips" or short relapses in which I felt compelled to touch the stove of addiction for an hour or two to see if it was still hot. It was.

Each time this happened, I built motivation to move forward in my recovery. After several years of only partially committing to the suggestions of the recovery fellowship and paying the price for my complacency, my motivation was strong enough to do everything that was suggested.

For the family member, Preparation may look like finding local Al-Anon meetings, looking for a counselor who has experience with families and addiction, or deciding to finally tell the rest of the family what has really been going on. As with the addict, this shows a new willingness to change, but no change has happened yet. In fact, many people get to the Preparation stage and then go right back to Precontemplation.

Why would a family member give up their own progress? One reason is that change can be scary. We have been using our old coping skills for a reason: they seemed like our best bet for a long time, even if they weren't perfect. We often fear what could happen if we stop using them, even if we don't like the results we've been getting. Because of this, it's easy to formulate new plans and then decide to back out. This may be as simple as continually putting off attendance at that first meeting or as drastic as going back to saying, "They're the one with a problem. I don't need recovery." To avoid this, cultivate self-awareness and seek feedback from people who can see your situations and reactions objectively. If you are slipping back into Precontemplation, try to realize what has happened and get back on track. If family members can do that, then they can move into the next stage.

Action

This is the moment everyone has been waiting for: the Action stage. Action is when the new plans are tried and new behaviors adopted. In the case of the tightening jeans, I finally start working out regularly, choosing healthier foods, and I may make and keep appointments with a personal trainer. I am feeling great about the new choices I am making for my health. For the person with the addiction, this may look like going to treatment or seeing a counselor regularly, attending meetings, starting the 12 Steps or SMART workbook, or simply cutting down or stopping addictive behavior for a time. At this point, there may be a lot of energy behind the change. Family members might hear their loved one say things like, "That was a great meeting," "My sponsor tells me I'm doing well," or, "It's been two months since my last drink."

In my case, the Action involved going to my first meetings. I was trying out something new and I had hope, but I was also uncertain if this was for me. What had changed from before is that I was willing to take the actions to find out. My wife was encouraged. Neither of us knew what to expect but we had heard that this could work. I bought a couple of books that were suggested by the fellowship and I started reading them regularly, studying them for clues as to what might help me. I compared what I was reading to what I had been through, noting the differences as much as the similarities. I talked in the meetings and listened for others' experience as well as their responses to what I shared. Most importantly, I started changing my behaviors at home. I stopped addictive acting out and alternated between confidence that this change would last for the rest of my life and fear at the idea of living another day without my addiction for relief. I trudged forward, but Action is not always easy.

This is important for families to understand to the best of their ability: entering the Action stage in recovery can be the most challenging thing the person with the addiction has ever done. To paraphrase a colleague, "Someone newly sober is suffering when they don't use." From the outside, it may look easy. In fact, some people early in recovery fear disappointing the family or feel guilt and shame for all the problems they've caused, so they hide their struggles at this stage. They may feel uncertain that they can keep it up but don't want to scare the people they love, so they only talk about how well it's going. Others wear their suffering on their sleeves. I alternated between these approaches in early recovery.

Sometimes the Action stage feels easy at first, a condition known in AA as "the pink cloud." This state of ease is known to be fragile and temporary, to the point that some say, "If you're on the pink cloud, pack a pink parachute." In other words, don't get lulled into complacency if the Action stage seems easy at first. As a family member, you may feel so relieved and scared at the same time that you are tempted to think, "They've got this. I know when they set their mind to something, they get it done, so they will surely be okay now." Unfortunately, this is not so. Action is new and more fragile than it looks. You would do best to focus on your own transition into Action rather than counting on someone newly sober to carry the family's hopes.

Family members can see themselves entering the Action stage as they start to make positive changes in their own lives regardless of what the person with addiction does. They may attend their first few Al-Anon meetings, set and keep a healthy boundary, or engage in self-care. These new actions can feel scary and positive at the same time. The family may start to taste relief for the first time in a while as they do something different and observe the results. Family members and others close to the person with the addiction may get excited to see that change is finally happening. Unfortunately, we are not out of the woods yet.

It is all too easy to slip from Action back to Precontemplation because the Action stage is like trying on a new pair of shoes. You are walking around the store, feeling if the shoes are comfortable, trying to decide if you like the way they look, and if these shoes will become yours. In other words, trying new action doesn't mean that long-term change has been accomplished. In fact, it is very easy to fall back into previous habits. Remember how I was going to the gym in my fitness example? Well, the business model for a gym is based on the reality that lots of people will sign up for a membership, start working out, and then quickly or slowly fall back into their old habits. If everyone who signed up at your local gym showed up regularly, the gym would run out of room.

If you are at this stage, you may notice that you have an expectation that positive change on your part should start to produce the change you want in the person with the addiction. This is a return to the "Precontemplation thinking" that you have control over their addiction and related behavior. It's true that addiction affects everyone around the person with the addiction, and recovery has the capacity to do the same[2], but this does not mean that your efforts will necessarily produce the changes you want in those around you. In fact, they may resist and resent your recovery when you start out. Alternatively, they may not even notice the changes you are making. Thus, it is important to keep your focus on recovering for yourself and allowing others the dignity to make their own choices. If you can do this and stay in the Action stage for long enough, then the next stage beckons. Notice that unlike all the other stage transitions, this one is born out of positive feelings coming from taking action rather than negative feelings from staying in painful behaviors.

Maintenance

The final stage is Maintenance, and for people seeking to make positive changes in their lives, it is the Holy Grail. Families in the Maintenance stage see the once-new actions they are taking become the new normal. To finish the example of my fitness journey, this is the stage when going to the gym, eating healthy, and other fitness behaviors are just part of my day rather than new, exciting behaviors.

It has become this way in my recovery. I don't think about whether meetings are something I want to keep doing. I just assume that they are. My spiritual life is no longer a thing of novelty. While I remain grateful for the life my recovery has made possible, it also seems normal now. One bit of external feedback that tells me I'm in Maintenance is that the people around me are no longer excited or surprised when I engage in my recovery activity. If I say I am going to a recovery fellowship meeting, no one says, "Good for you!" or, "But we were going to go out to dinner!" They say, "Okay. See you when you get back." We all take for granted that this is part of my life.

This happened slowly for me. Part of me remained skeptical of the whole "recovery thing" and part of me wanted nothing to do with certain aspects of the suggestions I heard at meetings. Thus, each new recovery action took a long time to become an accepted and regular part of my life. Once the initial flush of desperation and adventure wore off, I was left with the reality that this was to be my life moving forward, so any part I hadn't fully accepted was vulnerable to being dropped. However, as I became more and more convinced that I was seeing positive things in my life as a result of my recovery, and as my "slips" showed me that my issues could only be kept at bay with consistent action at a certain level, I began to settle into my life as a guy in recovery. Over time, my family got used to me going to meetings, reading program literature, and talking to others in recovery on a regular basis. Sometimes, recovery seemed like the backdrop to my life, other times it seemed like the foundation, but it was always there, no longer strange and remarkable, just "what we do around here." This was helpful in that it would now be remarkable and jarring *not* to engage in recovery. Everyone would notice that I had slowed or stopped, and someone would likely comment even if I was hoping they wouldn't notice. While my recovery is always up to me, it's nice to know that being in this stage of my recovery means I have that extra bit of accountability.

The Maintenance stage is not bulletproof, though. As with the earlier stages, it is possible to fall all the way back to Precontemplation. This is especially true with recovery, because recovery involves ongoing growth, and there is always a little discomfort before new freedom. To avoid this discomfort, the mind may trick itself into complacency, which leads to stagnation, and then a slide into old thinking and behaviors. The reasons for making changes in the first place may be minimized or forgotten. When considering a return to old behaviors, the thought may be, "It wasn't that bad," or, "Just this once." For the family member, this may be a thought that an important boundary can be relaxed just one time despite there being little evidence of change in the person with addiction.

For instance, the family member may be afraid of conflict and think, "I don't want her to be upset with me. It can't hurt to give her my credit card if she promises to be responsible with it." This may even go well for the first couple of times, and the family member starts to think they were making a big deal out of nothing, or that any new changes must be permanent despite long experience that says otherwise. Finally, they get burned and wonder how they got into the same old position all over again.

The easiest way for family members to slide into Precontemplation is to think that because the person with the addiction is doing well, that the family no longer needs to work on their own recovery. Families who would be alarmed if their addicted loved one stopped going to meetings or working on their recovery find themselves stopping the same activities in their own lives. Not surprisingly, when we do the same old things, we get the same old results, so if the family returns to its previous patterns, such as not seeking support around addiction, then they will likely get the same results they used to get, such as worrying, spinning their wheels with unhelpful actions and attitudes, and feeling helpless.

Luckily, the longer Maintenance is practiced, the easier it is to return to it from any earlier stage. For instance, let's say I am tempted to engage in one of my old codependent behaviors with my daughter. I may next think that I should pray about it instead, take a few moments to do so with a special request to be given the right actions instead of my old reactions, and then follow any direction I feel coming back. If I follow this course, I usually feel better and don't need to use my old behaviors.

Notice that in this process, I went from Precontemplation to Contemplation, then used Preparation to launch into Action, and was back in Maintenance. The whole thing could have taken only a few seconds and no one else might even know about what was going on in my head, but I was able to recognize that I was off course and reconnect with my recovery tools and behaviors before plunging into more self-made misery.

What can all of this tell us? One simple takeaway is that human behavior is hard to change even when a person desperately wants the change to happen. This is true for anyone making any change, but some changes have more "friction" to them than others. This refers to internal and external barriers to making the desired change. In the case of addiction, the internal friction around stopping the addictive behavior is extremely high, as we saw in the section on addiction and the brain. At the same time, helpful internal friction grows as the addictive behavior pushes the afflicted person further and further from their values and self-respect. This encourages change. Having these opposing forces at play makes someone with addiction vulnerable to bouncing around the various stages of change during any attempt at recovery. If you are watching this happen in your loved one, it is easy to become frustrated and scared at any return to a previous stage.

Instead, let me suggest compassion. Everyone with an addiction is familiar with the internal conflict that comes with part of them wanting to stop the addictive behavior and part of them urging them forward. As a client once said in family group, "Addiction is all-out war with yourself."

Having compassion for everyone, including yourself, in this difficult process will not only be kind and supportive, but will also give an opportunity to build relationships with your loved ones and yourself.

Recovery and Relapse

Now we come to the two big "R's" of addiction: Recovery and Relapse. Everyone hopes for the first one and fears the second. What is less commonly recognized is that both things apply just as much to family members. Earlier in this book, we looked at the family's need for recovery and what this might generally look like, so this section will challenge you to explore what it may look like more specifically in your case, and then will talk about the potential dangers of relapse into your old behaviors and how this can be avoided.

To recover is to get something back that was lost or stolen, or to return to a state of higher functioning after spending some time in a state of lower functioning. Often around addiction, many things feel lost or stolen. The most important of these include not so much the possessions and money, but things like safety, trust, self-respect, peace of mind, sleep, health, and a general sense of wellbeing. The loss of these things can embody the aforementioned state of lower functioning.

Thus, recovery involves returning to higher functioning through:

- regaining a sense of safety
- rebuilding trust in self and others
- growing self-respect
- increasing peace of mind
- sleeping better
- becoming healthier
- feeling a deeper sense of wellbeing

While you may have been wishing your loved one would return to or achieve each of these things by putting their addictive behavior aside, I should warn you that they often don't happen automatically just because someone gets and stays sober. They are likely to get a little better through letting addictive behavior go, but high functioning takes dedicated work, and you can't do it for them. Instead, let's consider how you can move toward the things on that list yourself.

Safety

What can you do to increase your sense of safety? Perhaps there are changes you can make to your life, new boundaries you can set, or old ones you can keep. Maybe it's not the outside circumstances that cause you to feel unsafe, but instead there are changes to be made inside. Therapy around old fears may be the ticket, or perhaps you can find greater relief through engaging in the written work and mentorship available in recovery fellowships.

Trust

How can you rebuild trust in yourself and others? Let's look at rebuilding trust in yourself first. This involves keeping your word not only to others, but also to yourself. If you say you will take some time for self-care, then following through will help you trust yourself a little bit more. Going to a recovery fellowship meeting is a signal that you value and care for yourself, which is another way to build trust internally. One of the most important ways to build trust with yourself and others is by keeping a boundary. Even if your loved one doesn't like your boundaries and doesn't want you to keep them, you are nonetheless showing you are trustworthy when you keep them, because it signals that you are true to your word. This is also a strong signal to yourself that you will protect yourself and your values.

Rebuilding trust in others takes time and experimentation. At first, extend trust in small things that are not as important to you. If trust is broken on these, not as much is lost, although you may feel grief, frustration, or anger because you got your hopes up and let your guard down. Be clear with the other person about what emotions came up for you when trust was broken and how this affects your trust level in them, but there is no profit in trying to lecture them into changing their behavior. It will be up to them to change or not. If you feel safe enough to extend trust later, then do so with something small again. If they can hold up their end this time, then a little trust has been built. This may lead to other times of extending trust in little things until they have shown through action that they are trustworthy with bigger things. It is not up to you to be trusting so they feel better. It is up to them to be trustworthy so both of you can feel better.

Self-Respect

By keeping boundaries and extending trust only when you feel safe enough to do so, you are also starting to grow your self-respect. Think of some other ways you can build respect for yourself. It may help to know your core values as a person. Think of values such as honesty, kindness, love of beauty, fairness, spirituality. Notice which ones stand out as most important to you. If you aren't sure, you might skip ahead to Chapter Nine and read the section on strengths.

Having seen your core values, how do you best express and, if necessary, defend them? It may help to start by speaking up for the ones you care most about. If love is most important to you, then use this to determine your next action, asking yourself, "What is the most loving thing I can do in this situation? How can I most clearly express my love?" This can get you away from asking yourself what action is most likely to get the outcome you desire, because none of us can perfectly predict that. Instead try to take actions that connect most with your deepest self. This is more likely to lead to self-respect regardless of how things turn out.

Peace of Mind

Doing so can in turn lead to greater peace of mind. Try to think of other ways you can increase your peace of mind. How about working on letting go? As always, I don't mean you have to kick your loved ones to the curb. Instead, imagine you can let them be responsible for their own feelings and actions while you take full responsibility for yours.

What's that you say? You already take full responsibility for your feelings? Check to see if you ever tell yourself that if they acted better you would feel better. If so, then you are making them at least partly responsible for your feelings. Do you act as though it is your job to make things easier for them? That would mean you are taking responsibility for their feelings. The more you can let this go, the greater your peace of mind. Consider that instead of taking responsibility for them, you could take a yoga class instead, or perhaps you could take that vacation that you keep postponing because you were afraid they would fall apart as soon as you're gone.

Sleep

Another factor to consider is how to get better sleep. Sleep researcher Matthew Walker talks about sleep as something essential that many people treat as a luxury, one of the most important things we can do for our brains and health.[3] Unfortunately, many family members find themselves with sleep issues as a response to the stress of dealing with addiction in a loved one. As a result, many family members think that the key to getting better sleep is for their addicted loved one to be doing better. Instead, I will suggest that working on your recovery will be the key. This allows you to let go of anxiety and thus get your quality of sleep untethered from your loved one's ups and downs. I'm sure a few people lost sleep over me in my active addiction, but I can assure you that I would never want this for the people who love me. I want them to be okay no matter how I'm doing, so consider letting yourself off the hook and getting some well-deserved rest.

Health

This will help to increase your overall health[3], but there are many other facets to health. You might want to contribute to your self-care through regular exercise, eating healthy meals, taking a spa day, or any other thing that helps you demonstrate better care for your health. What are some ways you want to do this? Is there an area in which you have been neglectful of your physical wellbeing? This is especially important if you have been telling yourself that you can't take proper care of yourself because your loved one needs help or if you have overlooked your own needs because you were so focused on the needs of another.

Don't forget about tending to your mental health. This can include counseling, recovery fellowships, meditation, reading something uplifting or inspiring, listening to relaxing music, finding podcasts and other recordings of inspirational people, or any other thing that helps you mentally. Binge watching shows or other activities that only help you tune out will not do the trick. Even though they may help you temporarily relax and escape, they will not provide the psychological nourishment to increase your mental health.

Wellbeing

Finally, let's look at how you can increase your overall sense of wellbeing. This extends beyond just knowing you and your loved ones are safe, and moves into the deeper territory of feeling a sense of meaning in your life. If this sense of meaning is mostly centered on taking care of your loved ones, consider expanding your horizons. One of the greatest ways people find meaning in their lives is through service[4], and there are many opportunities for service in our world. From local, national, and worldwide volunteer organizations to recovery fellowships to being there for a friend in need, there are many ways to give of yourself to something that inspires you.

For some people, spirituality is an important source of their wellbeing. My definition of spirituality for recovery is "a deep sense of connection to something greater than yourself." This sense of connection is vital to humans, and there are many ways to experience it. Regular spiritual practice has many benefits, and could take the form of prayer, meditation, spiritual fellowship, or a regular gratitude practice. It might mean nature walks that remind you of your connection to everything or it may be through an organized religion practiced at a place of worship. Whatever form it takes, this can be an important way to cultivate your sense of inner peace and life satisfaction by creating a sense of direction and connection.

Relapse

Relapse is the return to a state of lesser health after a period of higher functioning. It happens so often around addiction that some consider it a normal part of the recovery process. Others say this is defeatist thinking and even gives people an excuse to use again. However you view it, relapse is a possibility that everyone must face.

Relapse rates for addiction are about the same as other chronic health conditions such as diabetes or asthma[5], but addiction relapse is often judged through a moral rather than medical lens. It is too often seen as a betrayal rather than as an unfortunate event that requires additional care.

When I struggled to maintain sobriety early in my journey, the people around me sometimes reacted with tears or shook their heads. More often they showed compassion, but I judged my own relapses harshly, disappointed in myself and fearful that I would never achieve lasting sobriety. As a misguided coping mechanism, I sometimes looked down on others who relapsed. I bought into the idea that they didn't want it enough. I took a while to recognize that they, like me, are on a long journey of recovery with an uncertain destination. It took even longer to see that we are all suffering from a brain condition we would never have chosen, and that many such conditions involve relapse. I don't know if my personal relapse rate would have changed if I had a better understanding of addiction, but I feel certain that there would have been less anguish and distress for everyone involved if we had known more about these things.

Those who love someone with an addiction must be aware of the possibility of relapse in themselves as well. In other words, family members are just as prone to a return to less functional behaviors as the person with addiction, even if they have been doing well for some time.

Take a moment to consider what a relapse in your attitudes and behaviors would look like. What familiar thinking pattern have you fallen back on in the past? If you are unsure, here are some questions to consider:

- Have you thought that your loved would finally be okay if you could only control or protect them?
- Have you tried to get other people to treat your loved one a certain way in order to get the outcome you desire?
- Have you tried to rescue your loved one from the natural consequences of their own actions?
- Have you gotten a feeling that you are being manipulated but ignored it?
- Have you been afraid to set boundaries?

- Have you set boundaries but then let them go or let yourself be talked out of them?
- Have you tried to force solutions because you couldn't stand the uncertainty?
- Have you let your self-care go so that you could care for someone who doesn't seem to want it or who presents themselves as helpless when they could in fact help themselves?
- Have you told yourself that you are the only person your loved one has even though they could have support from many sources if they would only ask?

Any and all of these may be relapse behaviors for family members. If you don't find yourself in the things listed above, then take some time and write down your own relapse behaviors so you can recognize them when they crop up.

In AA, it's been said that drinking is the last thing that happens in a person's relapse pattern. This means that there is often a period in which other emotions, attitudes, and behaviors start to show up in a progression that leads to the relapse. As a family member, this applies just as much to you and your own relapse behaviors.

Let's look at an example: As a family member, my relapse behavior might be to lose my temper and say things I regret. Before I get to this point, I will likely feel, think, and do things that lead me to angry acting-out behaviors. It could all start with me feeling fear when my loved one goes out without telling me where they will be. At first, I decide that when they return I'll try to be supportive by burying the fear and pretending that I have all the faith in the world in them. I don't see that I am being dishonest by pretending to feel better than I really do. Next, I start to feel grumpy that no one notices that I'm not doing well. I tell myself that if my loved one would behave properly then I wouldn't have to feel this way. I start asking them leading questions to find reassurance that they are working on their recovery. They tell me they are doing fine but I don't believe them, and my agitation grows. I try even harder to get them to be the way I want, telling myself it's for their own good. This starts to grate on them, and they say or do something that reminds me too much of how they were in active addiction. Finally, I blow up, which is my relapse behavior. It feels like my anger came out of nowhere and I'm dismayed afterward at how things turned bad so quickly.

Looking at the above anecdote, there were several points at which I could have interrupted my process. When I felt the initial fear, I could have acknowledged that I was having a natural reaction and journaled about it, talked to someone in my recovery fellowship, or prayed about it. I could have remembered that I can't control my loved one's actions, but that it's okay to kindly tell them that I'm having trouble trusting them. I might have reminded myself that other people can't read my mind, so if I want acknowledgment of something, I'll have to speak up about it. Even if I had done this, I would have to remember that they may not have given me the response I want. I wouldn't have to be upset at this, because they are no more responsible for my feelings than I am for theirs. If I didn't like what I was hearing, I could have worked on my own acceptance rather than pushing harder to get what I want out of them. If I was telling myself, "It's for their own good," I might have done better to remember that I am no one else's higher power and I may not know what is best for them. If I still blew up after all my best efforts, I could go back and examine what I missed in my own thinking and behavior so that I could learn and grow from the experience.

You may notice that none of these things requires my loved one to change their behavior. My relapse is not really about them, so getting them to change is not the solution.

If you see yourself in this example or can think of what your own relapse would look like, it may make it easier to have compassion and patience for yourself and your loved one. This is especially helpful if they struggle to stay sober. Feeling fear and upset when someone close to you stumbles is understandable, so I encourage you to seek extra support and double down on your own recovery if this happens. It may help to understand that if your loved one relapses, it doesn't mean they never wanted sobriety in the first place, or that they will never get it.

In fact, many people do not get sober on the first try. I certainly didn't, but each time I relapsed, I learned something. If nothing else, I saw that I am not as self-sufficient as I thought. I took some convincing on this one because of my old belief that I had to look out for myself, and that even the most loving and well-intentioned people in my life couldn't be trusted to keep me safe. Therefore, the idea of accepting help was scary and I tended to try to do everything on my own. As a result, I showed up at a recovery fellowship meeting every week but I didn't do all the things I was told to do, especially those that required me to rely on anything or anyone outside of myself. I thought I would be a shining example of recovery by doing it my way. Instead, I became a shining example of how not to stay continuously sober. With each relapse, I became more willing, until I was so willing that I did everything suggested in my program of recovery, and I have been sober ever since.

I learned some other valuable lessons through relapse. Each time I got back up from scraping my knees, I learned that I never have to give up on my recovery. I learned greater compassion for others who are still in the grip of the disease. I learned that my lifelong stubbornness and perseverance, which kept my addiction going for a long time, could also be applied to my recovery. I learned that others will not automatically abandon me if I admit my struggles. I learned that surrendering to the recovery process does not mean giving up. Perhaps the most important lesson I learned is that accepting help and following direction can be safe. Without my relapses, I might never have seen these things, and thus would have missed out on seeing myself as I do today.

Next, we'll tackle the questions family members most often ask me about relapse: "What can I do if I see my loved one heading for relapse? What can I do if I suspect or even know it's already happened?"

If you believe you see your loved one heading for relapse, you are well-advised to look at what kind of groundwork, if any, has been set out ahead of time. If you and your addicted loved one have agreed on boundaries around relapse and what your place is in this, then it's time to put plans into action. For instance, if you have all decided that you are to keep your loved one accountable and point out any signs of potential relapse, then now is the time to let your voice be heard. This can be done diplomatically and kindly (I like to think that any truth can be spoken with love and compassion) but it must be done. If you find you are not greeted with the thankful reception you hoped for, then it may be time to re-examine the boundaries or your comfort level with your role. Perhaps, on the other hand, you and your loved one have agreed that only some signs are to be pointed out and others can be ignored. If so, then you might want to make sure that what you about to say is something upon which you all agreed.

If you are like most families, though, nothing was discussed and agreed upon ahead of time. This means that your options are more limited. At best, you can ask if they are open to your observations and then respect whatever answer they give. You can offer to get them help, such as counseling, but once the offer is made, you have done what you can. Reminding them of the offer over and over becomes an attempt to control them and stands a better chance of driving a wedge between you than it does of helping them.

Keep in mind through all of this that it is never your responsibility to make sure they stay sober, even if you want it to be. While this may seem frustrating or scary, you have no power to make or break someone else's recovery. You can, however, set clear boundaries regarding what happens if they relapse. If you need help and ideas on this, see the section on effective boundaries later in this book.

If you are sure they are headed for disaster and they don't seem to want your input or help, then there are still a few things you can do. First and foremost, you can prepare yourself as best you can, in the same way that people prepare themselves when they get warning that a hurricane is headed their way. Lock down items that may be lost or damaged, both literally and metaphorically. Know where you will turn for support and start reaching out before things get bad.

Work on your recovery with all the energy you want to see your loved one devote to theirs. Double down on any parts of your life that help you relieve anxiety. Note that relieving anxiety is not the same as masking it or just distracting yourself from it. For instance, working 60+ hours a week is likely only distraction, whereas engaging in self-care and counseling are more likely to actually reduce the anxiety.

All of these suggestions apply as much or more if your loved one actually relapses. Once again, you can offer help. In this case, depending on the severity of the relapse, you can offer to get them treatment. If you think this is something you are willing to do, then it is a good idea to familiarize yourself with different options. The next chapter concerns itself with the many types of treatment available and what to expect from each. Armed with this knowledge, you might see what is available in your area, and even some places that are farther away if they seem like a better fit. As you can imagine, these decisions are harder to make in the middle of a crisis, so doing some exploration before your loved one relapses can pay dividends if they slip in their recovery. Think of this like taking out an insurance policy. You hope you never need it, but if you do, you're sure glad you made the investment.

Whether or not you decide to get involved in their treatment, if they relapse then it is time to keep boundaries. If you didn't set any before the relapse, it is vital to formulate them now, make them clear, and stick to them. This can be done lovingly but firmly, but no matter how your boundaries are expressed, they can make a big difference in how well your relationship to your loved one and the rest of the family will weather the relapse. Even if your loved one struggles more because of the boundaries or gets angry because you are keeping them, you are setting a foundation upon which the relationship can grow later. At the very least, if you keep your boundaries during the relapse, you will be keeping yourself and the people closest to you as safe as you can during the storm.

This is also the time to invest even more heavily in self-care. Rather than put all the focus on your loved on and the ups and downs of their relapse, take some of that energy and put it into making sure you are as good as you can be in difficult circumstances. Your loved one may or may not want your help, or they may not want the type of help you are willing to offer. There is one person, however, that you can get to safety and whom you can help grow: you.

Not only will this contribute to your wellbeing, it will also help the rest of the family since family functioning can be improved as any family member is doing better. Additionally, it may model self-care for other family members. Finally, it may signal to the person struggling with relapse that their addiction is not running the family dynamic. This can help them reduce guilt and shame, which gives them better odds of pulling back out, and it can take away any power or attention they might be trying to grab if they have a penchant for being self-destructive to skew the family dynamic.

If you are able to take some of these suggestions and implement them in your life, then relapse can be transformed from a seeming disaster into opportunity and inspiration for growth and change in your life, and perhaps the lives of the people you love who are struggling with addiction.

Chapter 4

What to Expect from Treatment

While the path of realistic hope does not demand that anyone else recover, many families will anxiously watch their addicted love one go in and out of treatment, each time crossing their fingers that "this is the one." This is a very common part of the recovery process, so I want to give you an insider's view of what happens, as someone who has worked for years in different roles in various treatment settings. Together, we'll explore what to expect if your loved one goes through this process. To do this, we'll examine whether treatment is worth the time, effort, and expense, if and how much the family needs to participate in treatment, discuss the various levels of care commonly available, and talk about what to expect at each level. Finally, we'll take a look at what to expect after treatment ends. Naturally, the family's role in each of these topics will be discussed.

Is Treatment Worthwhile?

To begin, we need to answer one of the basic questions many families have: does treatment really work and is it worth doing? Luckily, this is a question that has a lot of research to answer it. Here's the overview: most people who engage in treatment have and create fewer problems moving forward. This includes having fewer new legal problems, less drug use, better mental and physical health outcomes, better occupational outcomes, etc.[1] This is not the same as saying that everyone who enters treatment will be sober and problem-free for life. Addiction usually follows the predictable course of most chronic conditions: targeted symptoms improve dramatically while the person is in active treatment then return to an extent after treatment, but do not reach the previous levels of distress.[2] In my experience, most people stay sober while in treatment, especially in residential care. After they leave, some never look back as they embrace recovery wholeheartedly, while others can't wait to get back to using, but most continue their sobriety for a while, then have some ups and downs. They are nonetheless more willing to be honest, seek help faster, and are more motivated to be sober overall. Research shows that if people use alcohol after treatment, they have fewer episodes of drinking and typically drink less per episode.[3] With most chronic illnesses, such improvement in multiple areas of someone's life would be seen as a success and certainly worth the effort.

Unfortunately, addiction is generally judged differently. In America, total abstinence for life is the only standard that the average person uses, and this is what is most often promoted at any treatment center. Professionals know this is not realistic for any chronic illness, however, especially not for one that centers in the part of the brain where we make decisions. Thus, many who work in the field learn to judge outcomes based on progress rather than perfection. European treatment providers tend to focus more on a harm reduction model rather than a total abstinence model[4], and some American treatment providers will acknowledge that even if total abstinence is the goal, harm reduction is the more likely result. If we can move into seeing this as a reasonable and successful outcome, then there is an opportunity to remove some of the shaming and blaming as people struggle to overcome addiction.

This more realistic view may also help families understand why so many people need multiple rounds of treatment. Make no mistake, everyone involved wants the first treatment to be the last treatment. Perhaps the person with the addiction hopes it will be the last one inasmuch as everyone drops the subject and supports them in continuing to use, but this is no more realistic than the family member who wants to "put this behind us" and hopes the addiction will just go away after treatment.

Instead, I urge you to have a clear-eyed view that addiction treatment is about playing the long game. It may involve several attempts at formal treatment along with a few times of trying to attend recovery fellowships and following the suggestions there. Most of the people I know who are successful in keeping their addiction in remission took several attempts to achieve long-term sobriety. They know they are still vulnerable even decades into recovery, and many of them put daily work into keeping relapse at bay.

My own journey towards lasting sobriety was a long one. While I had embraced an addictive lifestyle in many ways, there was another part of me that desperately wanted to stop. I tried to convince myself to quit more times that I could possibly count, but this resolve would last minutes or hours, rarely more than a few days. I would hold out for a while and then change my mind for trivial reasons, returning to my previous behaviors or worse. When I finally decided to join my first recovery fellowship, I intended to be done for life. Nonetheless, I was less than enthusiastic about following the suggestions I heard there and so I tried picking and choosing which tenets of the recovery program I would follow. This got me better results than doing it alone, but I still relapsed every 6-18 months.

There were a few factors that caused this. First and foremost is the brain chemistry that I talk about earlier in this book. I didn't know anything about this at the time, but in hindsight, it dominated my life and caused me a lot of confusion. After all, I had lots of willpower in other areas of my life, so why couldn't I stick to the obvious decision to stop my addiction? Additionally, I had always seen myself as "Special Casey" for whom the normal rules did not apply. I now know that underneath this, I had a fear that I couldn't make it under the "normal rules," so I had to push back against them. I also feared that sobriety would remain forever out of my reach, so I was reluctant to give it my full effort lest I disappoint myself one more time.

On the other hand, the pain of staying stuck in a cycle of sobriety and relapse pushed me forward in recovery. After several years of this internal tug-of-war, I got to the point that I was sick of myself and the results I was getting, and I became willing to do everything I was told. I claim no perfection in this, but when I applied my willpower to recovery activity rather than just trying to avoid acting out, I was able to put together the sustained recovery I have enjoyed since 2006.

Over the course of this time, I found that many of the things I "had to do" in my recovery became things I "get to do," such as attending meetings with supportive people and utilizing the tools of recovery. Doing so allows me to bring greater serenity to any problem I face. The process of developing enough hope and motivation to sustain recovery took about seven years of meeting attendance and effort, and decades of active addiction before that.

I hope that hearing this part of my journey will help you see why treatment which lasts a few weeks seems to stand so little chance against a lifetime of addictive thinking. On the other hand, research shows that any amount of treatment is better than none, and that the longer someone remains in treatment, the better their odds are afterward.[4]

Most people with addiction need at least 90 days of treatment at residential and/or outpatient levels of care.[3] Like any disease, addiction is not of equal severity for everyone, and not everyone will respond the same to a given treatment type. Thus, while we can say that 90 days is a good start for most people, the actual length of any individual's treatment should be determined by their needs as they move forward. A given length of stay is also not a jail sentence where someone only has to mark time and then they are fixed. What happens during that time will largely be determined by the individual in treatment. As mentioned above, almost everyone benefits from treatment, but some benefit more than others because they are actively trying to get more out of it.

Luckily, it is a myth that someone has to "do it for themselves" and really want sobriety with all their heart in order to improve. The reality is that everyone with an addiction has part of them that wants to recover and part that wants to keep using or acting out. Every day they are in treatment reinforces the part that wants to stay sober. In some cases, the part that wants to keep going in addiction is so strong that it seems like no progress is being made and they don't want recovery at all. If that was true, however, they would leave. I've seen many people leave residential treatment early, and outpatient treatment dropout rates are particularly high[4], but most people stick it out.

Every day someone stays in treatment is a day they made a choice to stay sober. This choice is reinforced by seeing others do the same, by building community with others who want to stay sober, and by receiving encouragement from staff and peers for that choice. They also have a chance to see, hear, and perhaps gain insight into something that helps them stick with their decision.

Things may seem frustrating or even hopeless to the family whose loved one is kicking and screaming, breaking rules, refusing to participate, declaring their intention to use as soon as they get out, or sneaking drugs into treatment. Under such circumstances, it can help to know that even though the person in treatment may not seem to be getting much right now, they are planting seeds for the future. When they are ready to change, they will have the knowledge and experience of treatment to draw from. Even those who leave treatment early can benefit. They may need to scrape their knees up more to convince themselves that they want sobriety more than addiction, but many of them will return to treatment when they feel more ready.

Family Participation in Treatment

You may be wondering whether and how much you need to participate in your loved one's treatment in order for them to succeed. The short answer is that you don't need to participate at all, but it may be helpful if you do. I emphasize this because some family members show up out of obligation or even fear that if they don't participate, their loved one won't make it. It might be tempting to let you believe this so that you show up and get the benefits, but I'd rather see you participate because you understand that it will be helpful for you and the entire family.

Why do I say it isn't necessary? During my time of running family programs in a residential treatment setting, many of our clients never had anyone show up for a family counseling session or family workshop. A good number of them recovered just fine anyway. To take things a step further, there are homeless people who are getting sober as you read this. Many of them have no family support or formal treatment, let alone a family counseling session or workshop to attend. Thus, we see that no family support is necessary.

Can it be helpful? Absolutely, but not always in the way that family expects. Most family members think of themselves as engaging in treatment to help the person with the addiction. They rarely start out expecting to learn about themselves, tackle any of their own issues, or feel better even if their addicted loved one is still struggling. Nonetheless, if you are willing to put in the work, all of these rewards and more are waiting for you. I advocate for getting involved in your loved one's treatment in order to feel better and to improve the family dynamic and communication. The person with the addiction may or may not recover right away, but the family can benefit regardless.

Family involvement often includes family sessions with your loved one's counselor, family workshops, helping financially, taking phone calls from your loved one, and visitation. Let's look at each of these in a little detail.

In most cases, if your loved one is in treatment, you will be invited to participate in a family session with your loved one's counselor. This could be part of a treatment center's family workshop or may be a completely separate event, but it is a time to get some customized counseling for your family, and it can be a great opportunity to gain insight and learn how to move through difficult conversations together.

What happens in the session will be greatly influenced by the counselor's style and experience in working with families. When I am conducting a family session, my main focus is working on communication. If a family can learn to communicate better, they have a foundation to tackle any other issues and have a much better chance of finding resolution. I offer skills and opportunities for family members to become more honest about their emotions and thoughts around what has happened in addiction and how to move forward. I encourage the family to move away from the Identified Patient model and instead acknowledge that everyone in the family could use some help. If there are difficult issues to tackle, I try to provide a safe context and some guidance in moving through these conversations.

I have known some very talented counselors who are not comfortable working with families, and so family sessions are either avoided or don't seem terribly productive. If this seems to be the case, it doesn't mean your loved one isn't getting good treatment, but your family should have a few family counseling sessions after treatment with someone who is more comfortable and experienced with this work.

Even in such situations, you can still make the best of the treatment center's family sessions by going in with some goals and topics of your own while remaining open to what the counselor has in mind.

Self-awareness can be very helpful in formulating your goals. Notice if your purpose is to get your loved one to feel bad by hitting them with everything they have ever done wrong in active addiction, or if you want to get them to soothe your fears about the future by telling you detailed plans of how they will stay sober after treatment. Such underlying motives will likely undermine clear communication and relationship.

If you find yourself feeling such impulses, consider instead that you can clearly state what is going on for you. For instance, you might let your loved one know that you feel hurt and angry and that you don't trust them yet, or you could say that you are scared and wish you knew for sure that everyone would be okay in the future. These statements are more likely to open up dialogue with your loved one, who may be feeling many of the same things.

A great goal might be to improve communication and rebuild the relationship. Ways to move toward this could include working on your fears of being honest with each other, letting go of control, finding ways in which you each try to manipulate the other, and talking about what you appreciate in each other. If there are multiple generations, set a goal that everyone's voice is heard, perhaps starting with the youngest in the family since they are often given the least chance to talk about their point of view and feelings. Work on expressing your emotions honestly and safely and being able to respectfully hear others as they do the same. Set a goal to say how you want to see the relationship improve, not just how you want your loved one to change, and what you are willing to do to move toward that improvement. Avoid saying you will do "anything it takes." Instead, see if you can name specific changes or new actions you are willing to do.

Some counselors may ask you to write an impact letter in which you let your loved one know how you have been affected by their addiction. If so, try to avoid blaming and shaming, and instead focus on the emotions you felt and what you experienced. This can be a difficult balancing act if you are trying to determine how they take what you say, but you can cut through this difficulty if you remember that you don't get to decide how anyone takes what you say. You can only monitor your own intentions and then speak from your heart. If you are still feeling hurt and angry, claim that fact without thinking this should or shouldn't make them feel or act a certain way in response. Your job is simply to communicate your truth. The rest is out of your hands.

Family workshops will typically be more structured and include multiple families. Hopefully, they will be run by one or more counselors who are experienced and passionate about working with families. Expect to have group educational sessions, group counseling, group activities, and possibly a breakout family session with just your family and your loved one in who is in treatment.

Some treatment centers have a weekly family workshop in which families are welcome to attend as they are able. In this model, family members can attend several times over the course of a loved one's stay. Others have multi-day or even week-long workshops, with the families invited and scheduled in. This type will typically only happen once during the loved one's stay in treatment. I have run both styles and have found them to both be effective.

Family members who have been to multiple workshops at different treatment centers tell me that the quality, utility, and especially the overarching message, vary considerably. Some family programs deliver well-meaning messages that the family is responsible for the outcomes of the person with addiction, and that if the family can learn to make all the right moves and avoid all the wrong moves, then their loved one will recover. I have also had family members tell me that they felt shamed as they heard the family blamed for the disease. As I hope I have made clear, I strongly disagree with these ideas. I hope that if you find yourself facing these approaches, you disengage and seek outside counseling instead, preferably from a professional who has a more holistic and helpful view.

Now let's look at financial participation in treatment. Many people in active addiction find themselves using up all their financial resources to feed the addiction, losing jobs, or otherwise finding themselves without money for treatment.

There is a wide variety of treatment available at a wide variety of costs, and there is no easy way to be sure which one is the best for your loved one. Many of them can be expensive and insurance companies are not excited about paying, especially given that so many people need more than one round of treatment to sustain recovery. Even if insurance does provide coverage, a single round of treatment may involve paying the entire yearly deductible. Due to high demand, free treatment options often have a long wait even for those who meet the qualifications. Thus, families are often left having to make tough financial decisions in the middle of a medical, psychological, and/or emotional crisis, which is the worst time to make such decisions.

If you are in a loving relationship with someone who is addicted, it thus may make more sense to have a frank discussion with all the stakeholders (i.e., family who may be involved and the person with the addiction, if possible) before a crisis hits. Take time to talk about how treatment may be financed, what level of financial involvement, if any, various family members may have, and thus what types of treatment are realistic options. This is not pessimism, it is pragmatism. Such a discussion is unlikely to influence someone's decision to act out in their addiction, so don't be afraid to be open and honest about where you stand.

Avoid the temptation to use this as a way to get your addicted loved one to change, such as only offering options that you think they won't like or trying to use treatment as the bogeyman to scare them into sobriety. Conversely, you don't have to let the person with the addiction make all the treatment decisions when they are potentially spending your money. As previously mentioned, people don't have to be excited about treatment to benefit from it. In my experience, they are not more likely to stay sober just because they got to pick the place they go.

Above all, be honest with yourself. If you think you will probably give in when you see how bad your loved one's addiction has gotten, then don't draw lines in the sand about how you "aren't going to spend a penny on fixing their mess." If you don't know how you are likely to react, then you would do best to either state this up front or to do some inner exploration and recovery work to determine what you are and are not willing to do if a crisis hits.

If your loved one goes to treatment, especially residential treatment, paying directly for that treatment may not be the only cost involved. People who go to treatment may still have bills that need paying and/or day to day expenses with which they will need help. For instance, many treatment centers will include meals but your loved one may want to get snacks, toiletries, and cigarettes. You'll have to decide how much you are willing to contribute to this.

Helping to pay for cigarettes can be particularly hard for many families to swallow, but smoking rates in most treatment centers are over 90%. It can be hard for your loved one to resist that temptation to turn to a legal drug like nicotine, especially in an environment in which most others are smoking and much socializing happens in the smoking area. While it has been suggested that it is easier to quit everything at once, most people don't take on more than they have to, just like most people don't decide this is the time to quit caffeine. Instead, they lean more heavily on the legal and accepted drugs to help them get over the ones they are no longer allowed to use.

So, as a family member, what do you do? Do you decide this is the lesser of two evils and not the hill you need to die on? Do you draw a line in the sand because you are not going to contribute to another deadly addiction? There is no right answer except the one that works best for you.

All in all, think about how much you are willing to help your loved one financially, and then stick with your plan as best you can. Unexpected expenses may come up, but at least you can make some rational decisions ahead of time about the ones you can see coming.

Next, we'll look at participating through phone calls. Treatment centers typically restrict or forbid the use of cell phones and have scheduled phone times for clients to use the facility phones. Some centers restrict phone access until the client has been there for a certain period of time; others allow access from day one. Either way, you are likely to hear from your loved one eventually. They may be in withdrawal-induced selfishness or they may be trying to make up for lost time by being especially nice or tearfully apologetic, but chances are it won't be a routine social call.

As a family member, it can be easy to assume that whatever mood your loved one is in during that call is how they are feeling all day. You might also think that it gives you an accurate gauge of how treatment is going. This is unlikely. You are only getting a small slice of their day.

I've seen clients get depressed for an hour and that's when they happen to talk to their family, then a little while later they are laughing and playing a game with the community. Their family only got the emotional snapshot of the call and assumes their loved one is miserable all day. I have often seen a client's tone and body language shift dramatically as soon as they are on the phone with family, and then change again once they are off. Some clients have complained to me that they don't know why this happens and that they are frustrated that they can't talk to their family the way they are learning to talk in group and individual sessions.

Additionally, your loved one may be going out of their way to create a certain impression when they call. They may be phrasing things to play up how well they are doing in treatment or they may try to make sure you know how miserable they are. They sometimes do not even realize they are doing it.

Even if they aren't doing this, it's hard to be completely natural at such an uncertain time in someone's life. Your loved one may not have learned how to have an honest and open conversation with you yet about anything, let alone something that feels important.

To compound this, pretty much every client in a treatment center is grappling with guilt and shame, although they may not be conscious of it for some time. Some will attempt to avoid these uncomfortable feelings by trying to get family to let them off the hook about recovery. Thus, many calls home are really meant to build a case for why they don't need treatment anymore. This can come in the form of telling you about all the shortcomings of the treatment center and staff, or how they can't relate to the other clients because everyone else is either worse off or not as bad (they didn't use the same drugs in the same way, they are all young and have too many tattoos, they are all old and don't have enough tattoos, etc.). Some may complain that they are being told what to do all day, sometimes characterized as "being treated like a child." You may hear complaints that "this place is like a prison," although this usually only comes from people who have never been to prison. Alternately, your loved one may describe how they have done everything asked and learned all there is to learn, they now know how bad the problem really is and they know what they need to do, so it's time for them go out and put this new knowledge into practice in real life. All of this is known as "hitting the wall," and stereotypically happens around two weeks into the program, although it could come at almost any time.

No matter the approach, when your loved one starts into these lines of reasoning, they are probably looking for your support to leave the treatment center. They may ask you to help by coming to get them or at least by signing off on their plan to leave. Your best bet is to not engage in such conversations. Don't try to get them to change their mind. You can simply say that you aren't going to come get them. You don't need to justify your decision and you don't have to get them to agree that staying in treatment is best. While it is up to them whether they will stick it out or not, it is up to you whether you are going to support them leaving. No matter how much you insist that you don't want them to end treatment early, if you come get them, send money for travel, or provide a place to stay after they leave, your actions will clearly show that you support their decision to leave.

You may hear threats, such as saying they will leave anyway and go use if you don't come pick them up. This sort of emotional blackmail attempt is best thwarted by gently reminding them that they must make their own decisions and that you are not going to participate in anything you don't agree with, so you aren't pulling them out of treatment or supporting their leaving in any other way. If they won't talk about anything else, or you feel like you are likely to give in if you listen for too long, then remember that you are not obligated to stay on the phone or keep taking their calls. You can tell them that you will be happy to talk again when they can find a new subject of conversation.

Some families are worried not so much about what their loved one will say, but instead about what the family should say. They are concerned that they will say the wrong thing and undermine the treatment process. Luckily, you have no power to screw up someone else's recovery. If they are determined to get sober, you can't stop them. But what if they are ambivalent, as so many are? It is still not up to you, but in any scenario, I still advocate for total honesty rather than trying to find the perfect words. Remember that total honesty can be delivered in a calm and loving way, even if what you are saying is that you are frustrated, hurt, and/or angry at them. There is no need to censor the truth out of fear, just as there is no reason to magnify negative feelings in hopes that your loved one will be motivated by guilt or shame. Instead, you might try the simple guideline, "Mean what you say, say what you mean, but don't say it mean."

For those who fear to give their loved one bad news while they are in treatment, consider that there may be no better place for them to hear it. They are surrounded by the support of both professionals and peers who can help them see how to apply the tools of recovery they are being taught. It's a chance to see that they can handle whatever life brings them, especially if they have support. If you are still in doubt, you can try to contact the counselor(s) who are working with your loved one to get some guidance on how to present the bad news in the most loving way.

During visitation times, some of these same guidelines may also be helpful for talking with your loved one. Most important, though, is to just work on being as real as you can during the visit. If you are not comfortable being in the treatment setting, it's okay to admit this and work through it. If you are sad and scared to see them there, it's okay to talk about that, too. If you are thrilled and relieved, it's okay to talk about this, as well. In other words, it's okay to be honest and authentic no matter what you are feeling. Notice, though, if you are going on and on about your feelings or find yourself repeating the same things several times. If this is the case, you may be trying to get a desired response from them or you may be trying to fix them by coming up with just the right piece of advice or insight. Let this go. Just as you have every right to your feelings and reactions, so do they, and your role in the recovery process is not to be their counselor or sponsor. You just need to be you, so have a little visitation time with your loved one and do your best to enjoy each other's company.

Levels of Care

The term "level of care" is frequently used to differentiate between types of addiction treatment, sorted by intensity. Does your loved one need to go to a hospital to get professional medical help or do they need to start by meeting in a church basement with other laypeople who share their problem? How would you as a family member know? There are many different levels of care available, and it can seem like a maze of acronyms and jargon to the family member who just wants to help. You may hear various terms used such as: detox, RTC, IOP, PHP, SOP, individual counseling, recovery coaching, and recovery fellowships. This section will walk you through how the appropriate level of care is determined and what each one of those terms means and involves.

To begin, the level of care is ideally determined by the rule of "the least restrictive care that still meets client need." In other words, we want to preserve the dignity and freedom of the person suffering from addiction while still getting them what they require to get and stay better. Sounds simple, right? Of course, in practice this is difficult to determine and there is not one set of guidelines that professionals all agree should be used. Since many people use health insurance to help pay for treatment, the insurance companies also weigh in on the matter, often seeming to think more in terms of "the least *expensive* level of care," leading to a tug-of-war between treatment providers who believe the services they provide are vital and that clients need to remain in care for as long as possible, and insurance care managers who believe that costs are overblown for treatment that seems ineffective and unnecessary. Thus, the level of care is often a compromise between financial and clinical criteria.

To complicate things further, many people with addiction want to engage as little as possible when treatment is first proposed, so they try to find the level of care that requires the least amount of effort and change. You may find that your loved one initially agrees to go to treatment, then starts arguing for progressively lower levels of care until you wonder what difference will be made anyway. What starts as a discussion of where to get detoxified and get treatment for at least 30 days can quickly become downgraded to a commitment to go to recovery meetings, or just quit on their own. For family members who are uncertain about how all this works, it can be hard to counter such arguments or even know if they should try. To help with this, we will look at what each level of care means and what it entails.

Detoxification

The first level is Detoxification, often shortened to "detox." For alcohol or benzodiazepine use, this is most safely done in a facility with 24-hour medical staff, such as a treatment center or psychiatric hospital. This is because both alcohol and benzodiazepines are central nervous system depressants, and detoxification from these types of drugs can lead to seizures and death if not handled properly. Detox in a facility is also recommended for opiate use because detoxing from opiates is so uncomfortable that without medication, monitoring, and support, many people give up and go back to using partway through the process. Stimulants such as methamphetamine and cocaine have an uncomfortable detoxification process but there is little medical danger and many people make it through, so there is no real medical detox protocol. If your loved one checks into treatment for these drugs, they may skip the detox level of care and go straight to residential level of care (described below) although many places allow the person to rest or "crash" for a couple of days. Similarly, there is no medical detoxification procedure for THC (the active ingredient in marijuana and its derivatives), hallucinogens, and other drugs simply because there is little known medical risk and people can get through it if they feel sufficiently motivated.

Some treatment centers may officially admit everyone at "detox" level of care for a short time of observation regardless of which drugs they used, but no medical detoxification will be available unless they have been using alcohol, other depressants, or opiates. This still covers a great many people with addictions, since so many people use alcohol even if it isn't their main drug, and your loved one may have used it a lot more than you know.

In some cases, safe medical detoxification can be done at home under medical supervision, but this would only apply for someone who is at little risk and also has high motivation to quit. These determinations must be made by a medical professional who has experience and training in addiction and home detox protocols. If there is any uncertainty, it is always a safer bet to go with inpatient detox.

Detox will generally last three to seven days. Three days is usually the minimum because alcohol detox symptoms can take that long to show up full force. This may lead to complaints from your loved ones who say they are fine and don't know why they need their vitals taken so often, and who don't like having restrictions on their freedom. Just know that even if it turns out to be unnecessary, these precautions save lives. While your loved one is in detox, little will typically be required of them, although some facilities will allow those who feel ready to start engaging in the groups and classes.

Your loved one will likely be strongly encouraged to make a direct transition from detox to residential care. They may start trying to negotiate a "lighter sentence" by saying they are willing to do something from home but not commit to 30-90 days of residential treatment. Rather than trying to convince them to stay, you might consider saying that you will only support the treatment recommendations of the professionals. This gets you off the debating team and directs them back to talking with those of us who have education, training, and lots of experience with such conversations. No matter what arguments they make, know that by the time someone needs detox, their problem is bad enough that residential care is the next right step.

Residential Treatment

Residential treatment, or "RTC," is what most people think of when they imagine treatment or "rehab." It may also be called "inpatient care." This level of care involves the client (your loved one) living at the facility, typically for at least 30 days. This is so they don't become overwhelmed by the stresses of daily life while dealing with the stresses of getting sober, they don't experience many of the triggers and habits of their home environment, and they are surrounded by the constant support of both staff and fellow clients who are also in recovery. This last factor is one of the greatest sources of healing from addiction. People find it much easier to recover when they have social support, even more so when they feel identification with others who are trying to recover.[5] Residential treatment offers these benefits in a concentrated and constant dose. Someone who is ambivalent about recovery can find themselves surrounded by others with whom they can identify ("They did what I did"), who are now seeking change ("They seem willing"), and some of whom are already seeing positive effects from recovery ("If it worked for them, maybe it will work for me"). This is vital because most people with addictions have told themselves many times that they will slow or stop their using, only to find that they couldn't do it on their own. This can lead to losing hope and increasing shame, and shame is strongly associated with addictive behavior.[6, 7] Shame has also been shown to be a barrier to getting help.[7] Being around others who are learning to drop the shame can thus become a healing factor within itself.

Residential treatment typically involves various activities throughout the day, all of which are aimed at helping people with addiction heal and learn how to stay sober in the long term. While every program will have its own flavor, here is one way a day in RTC might be structured:

7:00 AM Wake up, begin preparing for the day

8:00 AM Breakfast

8:30 AM Clean room and living area

9:00 AM Morning Meditation group (entire community)

10:00 AM Process Group (community may break into smaller segments to work through, or "process," various issues)

11:00 AM Educational/Recovery Skills Group (entire community)

12:00 PM Lunch

1:00 PM Specialized Process Group (e.g. men in one group, women in another)

2:00 PM Yoga/Exercise

3:00 PM Study Time

4:00 PM Free Time

5:00 PM Dinner

6:00 PM Recovery Meeting

7:00 PM Free Time

10:00 PM Lights Out

Some of these activities will be constant, such as morning Meditation and Process Groups, while others will vary by day of the week, such as Relationships Group on Mondays, Life Skills on Tuesdays, etc.

Along with the all the group counseling in residential treatment, each client will also be assigned a primary counselor from the clinical team. Depending on the program, this may be anyone from an intern fresh out of school up to a licensed psychologist with a doctorate and decades of experience. Many higher-end treatment centers will advertise that all their counselors are master's or doctorate level, indicating a consistently high baseline of education. While formal knowledge is a major factor in counseling, it should be noted that experience is also vital, because someone with an associate's degree and years of experience likely knows more of the ins and outs of helping someone recover than a clinician with the ink still drying on their post-graduate degree.

All that being said, the most important factor in counseling is therapeutic rapport, which is a fancy way of saying how well the client and counselor connect. There is no way to predict this going in, but a good clinical director will learn something about each client before and shortly after they arrive in order to assign them to a counselor who would be a good fit. Therapeutic rapport can be helped by the fact that many counselors at a treatment center are in recovery themselves, giving them an additional layer of relatability.

Your loved one should also have regular contact with medical staff, which could be anything from a full-time psychiatrist overseeing several nurse practitioners and nurses, to a contracted doctor or nurse practitioner who stops in weekly to look everyone over. This medical care should include proper diagnosis and medication management of any mental health symptoms or co-occurring conditions. This can be a major benefit of residential treatment even if little other progress seems to be happening, because many psychiatric conditions are difficult to pin down and may go unrecognized altogether during active addiction. Thus, the chance to get sober while under regular observation presents an opportunity to find and address underlying mental health issues, which can give the client a much better shot at sobriety and happiness.

Recovery fellowships are another important part of the RTC experience. The level of focus on these will vary, but almost all treatment centers will include classes on fellowships and many hold meetings on campus. The vast majority of these will emphasize Alcoholics Anonymous [AA], and many centers give every client a copy of the AA basic text, commonly referred to as the Big Book. This is likely because AA is the foundational program that started the modern recovery movement, it has gotten prodigious results, and it has been shown to be the most effective and cost-efficient treatment method when compared to other therapeutic approaches.[8] Another big factor seems to be that people who have recovered through the AA program feel inspired to help others do the same. This leads many of them to start or help run treatment centers. Since they got sober through the AA program, they naturally see AA as the way for others to do the same.

While the core AA message does not say that it is the one and only way to recover, and in fact it says the opposite in several passages of the Big Book, a lot of people in AA believe there is nothing else that really works. Thus, many staff members feel a personal and professional imperative to get every client to utilize the AA program like they did. Similarly, many of your loved one's fellow clients will embrace AA and may strongly encourage other clients to do the same, creating a treatment culture in which "AA is the way." RTC facilities that do not use AA at all are rare and are often looked at with some skepticism by professionals, so it may be difficult to get insurance to cover them.

Your loved one's reaction to all this may vary. Some may find it troubling, others will cautiously explore it, and some may decide that it is what they have needed all along. No matter how they react, you can expect to hear something about AA when your loved one goes to treatment.

Some treatment centers also include other recovery fellowships, such as SMART Recovery, Celebrate Recovery, Sex and Love Addicts Anonymous, Codependents Anonymous, Adult Children of Alcoholics, etc. There may be specific tracks at the treatment center to focus on one or more of these fellowships, they may be offered as electives, or clients may be only informally encouraged to try some of these other approaches to recovery.

Many centers encourage family members to attend family fellowships such as Al-Anon, SMART Recovery Family & Friends, Nar-Anon, or Families Anonymous. There is a more detailed exploration of recovery fellowships later in this chapter.

Once your loved one has completed RTC, they may be told to go to the next level of care. This would be a Partial Hospitalization Program, or PHP. They may also be encouraged to live in a sober living house for a while rather than going directly back to their previous home environment. Sober living homes will be covered later in this chapter and may come into play in any of the levels of care after RTC.

Partial Hospitalization Program

Partial Hospitalization Program, or "PHP," means that the client attends a full day of programming at the treatment center, but now sleeps at home or in a sober living house. It is rare to find a stand-alone PHP program, but some treatment centers will start a client off with PHP on a case-by-case basis. It is much more common for treatment centers to offer this level of care only after your loved one has attended RTC for a while. In many cases, people are officially moved into PHP because the insurance company will only pay for a week or two of RTC, but the center staff believes that the client is likely to relapse outside of a controlled environment. In such cases, the treatment center makes some minor adjustments to the client's program and/or sleeping arrangements but still has them live on campus 24/7. Often, this transition is made so seamlessly that the client is not aware that anything has changed in their official status. This may be done because some clients will jump at the opportunity to sleep at home with the best of intentions, but quickly become distracted and stop showing up at the treatment center. Some will find that the lack of accountability or support is too much to handle so early in the process, and then they relapse.

IOP: Intensive Outpatient Program

The next level of care offered is Intensive Outpatient Program, most often called IOP. This level of care is intended to be integrated into normal life activities such as work, child-raising, or school. IOP is thus most often offered in the evening but there may also be day sessions offered. IOP is usually expected to incorporate 24 three-hour sessions, most commonly conducted three times per week for eight weeks. This level of care may be affiliated with a residential treatment center or may be a stand-alone program. Many of the participants in IOP will have just completed RTC or PHP and were told that this was their next step. Others will have sought treatment when they had less severe symptoms or life consequences and were told IOP was the place to start.

The three-hour sessions usually include some of the same elements found in residential treatment. Sessions will typically begin with a time for participants to check in about how they have been doing, followed by a process group, and then an educational presentation. Throw in a break or two, and the session is complete. As part of the overall program, there should be one or more individual counseling sessions, but possibly with less frequency than at residential treatment, and there may be a family component offered. Regular drug testing should be expected, especially since the clients in an IOP program live and work in "the outside world," unlike the residents in a treatment center.

Some IOP programs are now being offered online. This is a relatively new idea as of this writing, so there isn't much data to say how this compares in effectiveness, but it certainly offers convenience that can't be beat.

SOP: Supportive Outpatient Program

The next level of care after IOP is SOP, which stands for Supportive Outpatient Program. This is basically IOP but with less frequent sessions, perhaps one or two per week. SOP is not a frequently-used level of care, but if it can be found it will usually be through an IOP that allows the client to come in less often once they have completed the regular IOP program.

Individual Outpatient Counseling

The next stepdown in level of care would be individual outpatient counseling, typically done either in an office setting or through video and phone sessions. As mentioned above, individual counseling will have been happening in the context of all the other levels of care, but once a treatment program has been completed, one-on-one sessions may be the only professional help your loved one gets.

For some people, individual counseling will not be a stepdown, but may instead be the first level of care they try. Often, they want to talk to someone one-on-one rather than engaging in a group experience. This is understandable, but in most such situations I recommend they at least try one of the recovery fellowships rather than having individual sessions be their only support. In a certain number of cases, I have referred individual counseling clients to detox and RTC during the first session because it is clear that their problem is too severe for weekly counselling to be effective until after treatment. Thus, individual counseling may be the final stage in the professional treatment process, or it may be the starting point that acts as a gateway to a higher level of care if needed.

One great advantage of individual counseling is that it offers long-term support that may be vital to your loved one's recovery. Treatment settings are usually measured in weeks, which means that there are many issues that simply cannot be addressed given the limited time available. One of my supervisors at a 3- to 4-week treatment center told me that if an issue couldn't be resolved in two sessions, it would be best to focus on helping the client recognize that the issue was important to address, then refer them to longer-term counseling to do that therapeutic work after treatment.

As someone who provides individual counselling in both residential and outpatient settings, I have seen the role of each. In residential treatment, a counselor can address intense issues more quickly, knowing that the client has a lot of support in between sessions. Thus, the hardest issues may be addressed up front, knowing that this may be the only chance for a client who is unlikely to continue therapy after formal treatment has ended. In outpatient settings, there is an ability to spread the intensity over time and to gradually work through things that are unlikely to get resolved in time-limited treatment. Additionally, some clients find there are things they don't talk about in RTC or IOP, perhaps because there wasn't time, they felt too self-conscious, or they were dealing with more immediate crises that overshadowed the deeper issues.

Outpatient counseling is the first level of care where you, as a family member, can participate equally. This can be done both by finding your own counselor and by participating in family counseling. It can give you a source of professional insight and a place to talk about how the whole family has been affected, as well as how you have been impacted personally.

I recommend finding a counselor for yourself as soon as you realize your loved one is dealing with addiction, regardless of whether your loved one agrees to get help. Many family members don't realize how much they have been affected until they sit down to talk with someone who understands the issues at hand. As mentioned earlier, not every counselor has experience with addiction and family issues, so be sure to ask up front.

Some people with addiction prefer to have a counselor who is in recovery. My experience is that this is not necessary for someone to be a good addiction counselor, but most people who seek careers in addiction counseling have either been through it themselves or are closely connected to someone who has, such as a close family member. It is understandable that someone seeking recovery might want to know that their counselor has a deep personal understanding of their condition, especially if they fear judgment or feel shame about it. Since a sense of connection and teamwork is such an important part of the therapeutic process, I would leave this decision to your loved one.

Family counseling sessions, in which two or more family members are involved, can be very powerful. Such sessions are an opportunity to talk about things in a safe environment with guidance. For some families, communication about addiction breaks down in any other setting, so this may be invaluable. If the person with addiction cannot or will not participate, the family likely still has many things to work out. Not least of these are family disagreements about how to respond to the addiction and what will be best for the addicted person and the rest of the family. This may in turn bring out other issues that have been buried or glossed over in the family dynamic, such as who in the family tends to get the last word, who gets the most or least attention, who feels they need to take care of the others, who checks out when there is conflict, etc.

Not surprisingly, the level of enthusiasm among family members may vary considerably. Some family members may be heavily invested in making sure that the family dynamic stays the same while others think this is the time to make all the sweeping changes they've always wanted. I've found it is best to allow family members to participate to the extent they are willing and comfortable rather than trying to twist their arms into attending family counseling sessions. This is especially true of teen family members. While they may have much on their minds and hearts around their loved one's troubles, they could be pushed away from the process and shut down if they are forced into it. Instead, give them room and let them know that they are welcome to join if and when they are ready. Rather than trying to convince them that they need counseling, be a model of how adults can seek and accept help.

Recovery Coaching

The next level of care is recovery coaching. Like a Twelve Step sponsor, a recovery coach has been through similar challenges as their clients, but unlike sponsorship, this is a paid position. Part of what is being offered in exchange for that payment is a sense of camaraderie and mentorship, but there should also be a certain level of training. Recovery coaches do not offer counseling but can help their client find a good counselor. They may help with goal-setting and life skills, then provide motivation and accountability. This is very helpful for some people in early recovery who may have trouble in these areas but don't fully trust anyone who is not in recovery. Since many people in early recovery or active addiction struggle with finding and retaining hope and motivation, a recovery coach provides a living example of someone who can sustain these things while also helping the newly recovering person do the same.

It should be noted that recovery coaches are not licensed professionals, so there is much less oversight and standardization, and there is generally nothing to stop any given individual from calling themselves a recovery coach. As with all health fields, the requirements are largely left up to the individual states, so it would be wise to research what standards, if any, a person must meet in your state. Some states and organizations offer recovery coach certification, which provides some minimum requirements. For instance, in Texas, where I am currently writing, a certified recovery coach must be at least 18, have earned a high school diploma or GED, have gone through the same struggles as the people they will serve, and be willing to share their story to inspire others.[9]

Note: The next sections in this chapter cover resources that are not usually considered levels of care in their own right, but are all things that will likely make up part of your loved one's treatment. Each may be approached individually or within the context of the various levels of care, and they often complement each other.

Recovery Fellowships

For some readers recovery fellowships, otherwise known as mutual self-help groups, may be the only recovery help their loved one ever gets. It must be noted that there are some significant differences between these groups and any other type of help for addiction. Recovery fellowships, which are touched on in several sections of this book, are the cornerstone of most of the other levels of care and are often woven into the fabric of those other levels. As described above, many treatment options are based squarely on getting people to engage with and stay in recovery fellowships, most often Alcoholics Anonymous. Features found in all the fellowships include social support, guidelines and tools for sobriety, and the hope-building example of others who have gotten and stayed sober using these things.[11]

While some or all these same factors are present in most other levels of care, there are a few things that separate these groups from all the other levels. The first is that help is generally offered at no cost. While the group may "pass the hat" during the meeting, there is no need to ever give any money in order to receive any and all of the benefits. Another differentiator is that there is no requirement that this level of care ever end. Residential treatment, PHP, IOP, and SOP are all expected to follow standard lengths of treatment with minor variation. Individual counseling and recovery coaching are more open-ended about how long they will last, but there is still an expectation that these are finite relationships. Recovery fellowships, on the other hand, may be attended for life.

In fact, Twelve Step members actively and explicitly advocate for lifetime participation as the best way to stay sober. Some give dire warnings about what happens for those who stop. For instance, one social media meme said, "AA is like the Mafia: Once you join, you are family, but if you leave, you die." While this is not scientifically supported, there are countless relapse stories that begin with, "I stopped going to as many meetings." Thus, lifelong attendance is encouraged even if it is not strictly necessary for every person. After all, the only way to find out of you will be okay stopping is to stop, and thus dramatically increase your risk of relapse.

Luckily, there is more to motivate long-term attendance than fear. Recovery fellowships offer substantial and well-established benefits that can grow and deepen over time, especially for those who do all that is suggested, such as working through the Twelve Steps of AA or the four phases of SMART Recovery. Many members go through the complete process multiple times over the course of their recovery and find greater benefit each time. Even if they never use these tools, the constant social support, positive examples, direct mentorship, and accountability offered by attending meetings all help members stay away from addictive thinking and behavior. Another benefit to long-term attendance is the opportunity to help others who are newer to recovery or are struggling to maintain it. The positive effects of being helpful cannot be overstated. Being of selfless service in any context helps to create a sense of purpose in the world and in life, which is one of the major pillars of human happiness.[10] Helping someone to dramatically change their life in same way you were helped, seeing them learn and grow, and feeling like you played a part can all be immensely powerful.

A recent study showed that when members of four different recovery fellowships (AA, SMART, LifeRing Secular Recovery, and Women for Sobriety) were tracked over the course of year, all did about equally well as long as the participant expressed a desire to stay sober for life.[11] Not surprisingly, greater participation was also found to predict better outcomes, with each of the following increasing a person's odds: attending meetings recently, having one or more people in the fellowship that they can contact for support in between meetings, volunteering to help with the meetings, and leading a meeting within the past month. While the tools offered by each fellowship are important, the basic factors of committing to a lifetime of sobriety, gathering with others who have a similar experience and commitment, and getting involved in the process of the fellowship all seem to be the most important elements. Jumping from fellowship to fellowship gets lesser results and is correlated with less satisfaction.[11] Thus, while your loved one may need to try more than one fellowship to see where they feel most comfortable, once they find it, they will benefit from dedicating themselves to what it has to offer.

It should be noted that in the basic text of AA, the book does not say that members should join for life, instead taking the stance that if members want the benefit, they should attend the meetings and follow the suggestions. The basic text also warns against trying to talk people into participation, instead choosing to work only with those who seem interested and not ruining the chance to help someone later by forcing it on them today.[12] Similarly, SMART explicitly states that people are free to attend for as long they find it useful and that while some choose to be part of

SMART indefinitely, they can come and go at any time.[13] While individual members may lose sight of these ideas, it is good to know that the fellowships themselves are based on freedom of the individual to choose how much and what kind of help they want at any given time.

Unlike the higher levels of care, which may ask the family to participate, recovery fellowships do not require any level of family participation, but instead offer separate family fellowships. Almost every Twelve Step fellowship has an analogous family fellowship that may be integrated into the addiction fellowship, associated with it, or completely separate but friendly. For instance, Celebrate Recovery meetings are open to both people with addiction and their families, and then may split off into sub-groups for part of the meeting to allow different members to focus on their particular issues and perspectives. SMART Recovery Family & Friends has separate meetings but are considered to be a part of SMART. Al-Anon, started by wives of the early members of AA, is a completely separate fellowship that nonetheless acknowledges using a minor variation of AA's Twelve Steps, and which cooperates with AA.

It should be noted that there is no requirement that you participate in the same flavor of recovery as your loved one. They may love the Christian emphasis of Celebrate Recovery while you find that SMART Recovery Family & Friends' scientific perspective is a better fit for you. As mentioned earlier, I highly recommend finding a fellowship to attend no matter what your loved one chooses to do about their addiction. This is doubly true if they decide not to do anything or don't want to do enough to bring it under control.

One question I get from time to time is whether family members should attend recovery meetings with their addicted loved one. This usually only comes up in the early parts of someone's recovery, such as when the addicted person completes treatment and is trying to manage their transition to outside life. There is no right answer for everyone, but some people have found going to meetings together to be very helpful. For the person with the addiction, there can be a sense of support as well as a hope that the family members will gain greater understanding of addiction and recovery. For the family members, there is an opportunity to gain first-hand knowledge of what happens at meetings and a chance to hear the viewpoints of other people in recovery. All the intellectual understanding in the world can't replace the experience of seeing that your loved one is not alone in their journey, that others have thought and done the same things, and most importantly that those people have found a way to recover. This can be particularly helpful if your loved one is new to the process.

There are some pitfalls to be avoided, however. First and foremost, don't go to meetings with your loved one unless they have explicitly asked you to do so. If you are attending in order to check up on them or to impose support they did request, you are likely to do more harm than good to your relationship with them. If you want to get the benefits of going to addiction meetings but your loved one has not expressed interest in having you there, you can go to meetings they aren't attending. Always check to make sure the meetings you visit are designated as "open" meetings, which is to say that they are open to anyone who wants to attend, as opposed to "closed" meetings, which are only for those who identify as having the problem that fellowship is there to address. These designations should be apparent on meeting schedules. Note that even at open meetings, visitors who don't identify as having the problem are usually asked to only listen, although this may vary by the individual group. You can nonetheless talk to people before and after the meeting about your situation and you may find that members are happy to offer you encouragement and support.

If you are going to attend AA meetings, I highly recommend going to a birthday meeting. These are meetings in which group members are recognized for having achieved recovery milestones within that month. They may have gotten their first month or two sober or they may be celebrating years or decades. Each person who is celebrating a length of sober time may speak briefly about their journey and what helped them most. If your loved one is new to recovery, it can be uplifting to hear the voices of others who were once new and have sustained long-term sobriety. It can also be instructive to hear the progression in thinking and attitude that becomes apparent as you hear first from people with the shortest amounts of time and then work up through those with the longest.

On the flip side of all this, you are not obligated to attend meetings with your loved one just because they ask. They were able to get themselves to the liquor store, dealer's house, casino, etc. without your help or attendance, so they can make it to the meetings and sit through them without needing you there. If you go, go because you can feel it benefitting your recovery, not because you think it will save your loved one.

Sober Living Homes

Sober living homes, sometimes just called "sober living," "halfway houses," or other variations on this theme, are meant to be a transitional living situation, most often between residential treatment and fully living in the "outside world." Some people go to a sober living home for a few weeks as they rebuild their lives or start over in a new city, while others live in one for years because they find this is the best environment for them. While they are mostly associated with chemical addictions, I know someone who started a sober living home for food addiction, so you never know what's out there until you look.

A sober home can be chaotic yet supportive like no other living situation. Your loved one will have a chance to form bonds with their housemates that can last a lifetime. They will have opportunities to help others. They will have some of the same camaraderie found in treatment centers or at meetings. They may find that this is their ideal spot to take time and prepare for a new life of sobriety or they may move out as quickly as they can. They will likely see some people relapse, watch others run off with their latest soulmate, and see everyone struggle at some point. With any luck, they won't do too much of this themselves.

There is more variation in sober living homes than in any of the levels of care listed above because there is not a uniform definition of what even qualifies as a sober living home. There is also little current regulation, although there is a growing movement in some states to find ways to regulate sober living homes, and there are some voluntary certifications available. The only federal laws around sober living homes are non-discrimination laws that actually make it more difficult for states to regulate, so it is up to each individual state to take what action it can or cares to. Thus, the wide variation. You can find high-end homes that offer their own IOP, have recovery coaching, help clients find jobs or get back to school, organize outings, and have nicer amenities. Needless to say, these will be more expensive and may ask for a longer commitment up front, such as three month's rent. At the other end of the scale, someone might simply buy or rent a house and declare that to live there, you need to stay sober. This will cost a lot less money, may rent by the week, and will likely fall below the radar of any regulation. And then, there is everything in between. At a bare minimum, most houses will require a resident to attend meetings, some of which may be held at the house itself. Most places are owned and run by people in recovery, and the house manager at many a sober living house started as a resident there.

So, how to choose? First off, recognize that if your loved one wants your help to pay for sober living, you have a say in where they go. If not, then don't try to take control of the process, although you may offer an opinion if it is requested. Assuming you are helping with the finances, I advocate for a collaborative choice. One method I've seen work is for your loved one to pick several places they like in the price range you are willing to offer. Out of these, you pick out three that sound good to you. Your loved one then chooses one of those three. This allows both parties to have a hand in the decision. If your loved one is in RTC, the staff there may have sober living homes that they prefer. Some treatment centers have staff members whose job duties include lining clients up with sober living houses. Your loved one may also see others in their treatment cohort going to a particular house and thus base some of their preference on the idea of knowing people at that home already.

How much should you help them once they are in the sober living home? Some places will only allow family to help the resident for a set amount of time, such as 1-3 months, after which the resident must be self-supporting. Even if the home does not require this, it's a good idea to have a financial transition plan in place and clearly communicated ahead of time. For instance, you may be in a position to cover all of your loved one's expenses in the first month, two-thirds for the second month, one third on month three, and then they are on their own by the fourth month, whether they decide to continue with sober living or strike out on their own.

Some families say, "We'll make our house into the sober living home." This is generally a mistake. No matter what rules are agreed upon ahead of time, no matter what contracts are signed, no matter how good everyone's intentions are, we all tend to fall into familiar behaviors around familiar people, and this is especially true with family. Instead of your house becoming a sober home, it will tend to become a place of tension and conflict since you are not used to playing the role of house manager and your loved one is not used to seeing you in that way. Rules will start to fade or be fought over, one or both of you will use "that tone of voice," you and your loved one will start to push each other's boundaries and buttons. Thus, if you or your loved one think they need sober living, send them to an actual sober living house.

Medical Professionals

Medical professionals are an important part of addiction treatment no matter what level of care your loved one chooses as their beginning. Such professionals include psychiatrists, medical doctors, nurse practitioners, and nurses who specialize in addiction. As mentioned earlier, Detox and RTC will include contact with such professionals, but this should not be the only time your loved one works with them. At the very least, if your loved one has been using substances, they should have a medical consultation when they stop. Ideally, this should be an honest and thorough assessment with someone who is familiar with addiction issues and who can help ensure your loved one's health gets back on track. Regular check-ups should be a part of your loved one's addiction care moving forward. This is in part so that unforeseen or unrecognized side effects of the chemical use and its discontinuation don't sneak up on anyone, but also because routine medical visits are a part of good self-care, something many people with addiction neglect.

Additionally, it is very common to find that once active addiction is no longer in the way, underlying mental conditions can be more clearly seen or ruled out. Depression and anxiety are very common in early recovery. In some cases, these are a reaction to letting go of the acting-out behaviors, and in other cases they are long-running conditions suppressed or managed by the acting out. Either way, professional help, such as seeing a psychiatrist trained in addiction medicine, is warranted. Conditions such as bipolar, personality disorders, or psychosis may also be revealed and then treated.

It should be noted that some conditions may get significantly better as your loved one stays sober and, ideally, actively works on their recovery. They may find they no longer need antidepressants after a year or two sober, but this cannot safely be determined except in consultation with a prescribing professional. Too many people have found themselves returning to active addiction because they decided to go it alone with these medical decisions, such as discontinuing psychiatric medications without talking to their doctor.

I tell all my clients to let their medical professionals know up front that they have an addiction. For instance, whether I am seeing a dentist or going to the ER, I make sure it is clear on all the forms and in any medical interviews that I have addiction issues and will not take any narcotic medications.

This sometimes leads to interesting and at times very vulnerable conversations with medical professionals who have been affected by addiction personally. Most importantly, it is a way to keep myself and those I love safe by avoiding medications that could send me spiraling back into active addiction.

What to Expect After Treatment

While no one knows for sure what will happen after a given person goes through treatment, there are some basic things that one might expect. The first thing is that no matter how much they have been encouraged to continue using the tools and skills they were taught in treatment, this will likely be more challenging than they think. Second is that old symptoms and behaviors are likely to appear, but that this does not mean they are doomed to certain relapse. Third is that, for the family as much as the addicted person, this is a time when extra support should be sought.

While your loved one is in treatment, they will be told any number of times to continue the new behaviors they are learning. These behaviors will include staying closely connected to others who are recovering, attending recovery meetings, continuing self-exploration and reflection, reading literature related to sobriety, dealing with emotions as they come up, keeping a regular schedule, maintaining healthy eating and exercise, taking medications as directed, and anything else that has helped them stay sober while in treatment.

This is a struggle for many people, in part because of the force of habit. One of the best predictors of what a person will do in the future is what they have done in the past. This is likely because our brains constantly compare everything that we are currently experiencing to what we have experienced before. We then look for the most efficient ways to deal with what is in front of us or what we think is coming next. Habits act as shortcuts or templates in this process to help us move through our lives. The longer we have relied on a particular habit and the more effective it seems to be, the more likely we are to turn to it.

It may help to understand that this is not done based on any rationality or logic beyond the simple formula of "When I did this last time, I survived and possibly got a good reward." For your loved one, addiction started out as a reward so powerful that the subconscious brain has established it as a primary habit that can override any other. If they have been relying on this habit for months, years, or decades, it should be no surprise that a few weeks or even months of treatment will not eradicate it for good. Instead, treatment will work to establish new habits that lead to more enticing rewards for the subconscious brain, but those rewards take much longer to materialize than the quick hit of addiction. Once treatment ends and life returns to "normal," the brain's first instinct is to go back to all the old behaviors, and your loved one will have to work hard to push back against this tide.

Your loved one will have to find a balance between how they operated in the world before treatment and how they learned to operate during treatment. Some of them will question whether they really need to keep up all the changes. Others will try to keep their momentum but find that it's a lot harder than it looks. Perhaps they will find ways to replicate many parts of the treatment environment. For instance, they might surround themselves with peer support through attending recovery meetings and keeping in touch with those peers in between meetings. They may spend time reading recovery literature and start each day with meditation. They may see a counselor regularly. No matter how hard they work, though, they will start to feel the pull of emotional issues that are not fully resolved, daily responsibilities, and the distractions of life. Some of the habits of treatment will start to fade.

Ironically, this can happen more quickly if things are going well. Your loved one may find that their employment outlook is improving, family relationships are healing, and they are finding a comfortable place in their community. These may be all the things everyone hoped could happen in recovery. It can be easy for both the person with addiction and their family to focus on these rewards and lose sight of what made them possible, which is not only the fact of sobriety but also the daily work necessary to achieve and maintain it.

Family members may have to work equally hard to avoid falling back into all their old habits around addiction. I have seen too many family members start to work on their recovery while their loved one is struggling, only to let these efforts fade away when their loved one starts to get better. Soon enough, old attitudes and behaviors start to creep in, and the family members find they are once again relying on their loved one's wellbeing to dictate how the family is doing. This may seem benign while the addicted person is doing well, but recovery is not a straight line or a smooth path, especially right after treatment. As soon as the addicted person starts to waver or fall, the rest of the family starts into distress as a result. The solution to this is not to try to manage and control the addicted person's recovery. The solution is to work on the family's recovery instead.

A deeper reason that recovery work can get dropped after treatment is that it challenges people to learn and grow through self-examination and facing emotional issues. This may bring up issues have been buried or pushed aside in the crisis of active addiction, and perhaps things that were avoided long before addiction became an issue. It can seem easier to let recovery activity fade rather than tackle this work, so the mind begins to rationalize reasons why it isn't necessary once the immediate crisis is over.

While family members and people with addiction both succumb to this, it seems easier for families to fall into this trap since they are not the ones with as obvious a problem. Tempting as this may be, I urge you to stick with your recovery. It has the potential to bring you rewards such as peace in your heart that you may have assumed could only come if your loved one is sober.

If you start to see old behaviors and attitudes crop up in your loved one and yourself after treatment ends, you should not be surprised. Try not to jump at everything you see as if it is a sure sign of relapse. Both you and your loved one may have some adjusting to do and will experiment, whether consciously or not, with how to live in recovery. Even if your loved one has tried many times or perhaps had long stretches of abstinence in between relapses, each post-treatment period will present a new opportunity and framework in which to operate. This means that internal negotiation will take place, leading to varying external behaviors. You may find that you and your loved one become hypersensitive to the slightest hints of old behavior. Thus, the twitch of an eyebrow or a familiar look in your loved one's eye can leave you on edge as though all progress is lost. If you find yourself reacting this way, consider working harder on your recovery rather than watching them more closely.

I heard a story from someone who had recently left treatment, saying one of their family members accused them of relapse. They were initially upset at the accusation and couldn't imagine where it came from. They nonetheless engaged in the kind of self-examination they had learned in treatment and saw that they were letting some of their new habits such as prayer and meditation slip a little. Somehow, their family member, who was unaware of this, recognized a subtle return to old behaviors and mistook it for full relapse. The newly-sober person ended up being grateful for this difficult experience.

As a word of caution, the takeaway from this story is not that you should be looking for any little sign of old behaviors and then pointing it out in hopes of heading off a potential relapse. I have heard some people with addiction say this sort of constant observation and accusation became their reason to start using again, thinking, "If I'm being accused of it all the time I may as well do it." This is obviously not sound reasoning, but it is a reminder that it is not possible for you to keep someone else sober, especially not by jumping on everything they do.

In fact, before you set yourself up to watch their every move, remember that you can safely assume your loved one will be just as sensitive to your old looks, attitudes, and behaviors as you are to theirs. This is especially true if your behavior has seemed shaming or controlling to them in the past. They may see a look or hear a tone in your voice and jump to the conclusion that you have no faith or trust in them. It won't help that this likely reflects reality.

I've often heard both people in treatment and their families say they want to rebuild trust but don't know how. The simple answer is that trust comes when people feel safe. We can't will ourselves into a feeling of safety. The feeling of safety must come from experience, which means it will take time and effort. If a family member offers too much trust before they feel safe enough, then they will likely be on edge, perhaps not even realizing why. If the trust is then broken, it can feel devastating or infuriating. A better course may be for all involved to have patience and simply know that rushing the process will likely get everyone less of what they want in the long run.

Ben Franklin said, "If you want to be loved, be loving and loveable." In the same vein, if you want to be trusted, be trusting and trustworthy. This is easier said than done, but it starts with extending small bits of trust on low-stakes issues and seeing how your loved one does with it. It is equally important to be trustworthy, though. Many family members think of themselves as highly trustworthy, yet have not kept their word when they set boundaries and have not been honest about their feelings. For instance, if you say, "This is the last time I will tolerate this behavior," but continue to tolerate it, you are breaking trust. Your addicted loved one may be perfectly happy in the moment if you break trust this way, but they will notice and believe you less the next time. If you act like you trust them more than you really do, they will notice this, too.

Thus, I don't recommend trying to project confidence in them that you don't have. Instead, be honest. Understand that they may be watching your every move just as much as you may be watching theirs. Know that this only happens because you each care about the other's opinions and want to be connected. Be patient and kind with one another and yourself as you move through this difficult transitional period.

Something that can help during this time is to seek additional recovery. This could include going to extra meetings, making calls to members of your recovery group in between meetings, seeing a counselor for the first time or seeing your regular counselor more often, and engaging in additional self-care. This would be a good time to engage in the written work of your recovery fellowship, as this usually offers some of the deeper rewards of recovery. It is also a good time to both accept extra help from those around you and to be of service to others. This could remind you that your value to the world extends beyond trying to make sure your loved one is okay. Whatever support looks like to you, be sure to find it and accept it in this inevitably stressful time.

Chapter 5

Effective Communication, Feedback, and Boundaries

Most of the work I do with families around addiction comes down to working on communication. This is in part because when communication becomes open and honest, many issues start to move toward resolution. Where resolution does not come naturally, open and honest communication facilitates clarity about the problem and a better sense of how it may be addressed. Unfortunately, addiction tends to bring out secrecy and dishonesty instead. This is most obvious in the person with the addiction but often appears in family members as well, although it may be harder to see. Addiction also leads to fear and distrust, which are enemies of effective communication.

To make things worse, many families have a long history of addiction-impaired communication. Even if the addiction itself skips a generation or two, family patterns that developed to cope with it can get passed down to each new generation anyway. Sometimes this happens by example and other times it is taught directly. For instance, older family members may tell younger family members, "We don't air our dirty laundry in the street," or, "Stop crying, go get cleaned up, and come out with a smile on your face," or, "Don't go telling the neighbors what goes on in this house," or, "Dad wasn't drunk last night, he just felt sick." Such sayings train the next generation to keep secrets, or hide feelings and deny the truth. These are all factors that undermine good communication. Less overt teaching might include parents modeling secret-keeping, refusing to discuss addictive behavior, or simply not showing emotions when difficulties naturally arise in life.

I grew up with some of these ideas. In our house, it seemed forbidden to openly talk about, let alone challenge, my dad's alcohol use. Given that his drinking sometimes dominated our lives, everyone in the family was in a bind. There was something obviously wrong that could not be acknowledged, so hiding feelings became a coping strategy. This left our communication largely devoid of emotional content except for expressions of happiness when deemed appropriate. Anger was reserved for my dad, but this rule was not openly stated either. Thus, we had boundaries that were not clearly set, but instead were often discovered only when they were crossed.

My dad's mood set the emotional tone for the household, which meant that when he was drinking, all bets were off. One night when we were on vacation in a small cabin rental in the redwoods, he was up late and getting loud, yelling nonsense commands that everyone tried to obey. I thought he had lost his sanity and I expected orderlies to arrive any moment from a mental hospital to come take him away. We were able to fall asleep only after he finally passed out. The next morning, my parents said dad had not been feeling well the night before. No further explanation was given and it was never spoken of again.

This helped model a family culture of secrecy, denial, dishonesty, and silence. In short, we learned to unwittingly protect and enable my dad's addiction through our communication or lack thereof. Later in life, I would use these same patterns to protect my own addiction and encourage those around me to do the same.

First and foremost, I took on the idea that problems must be hidden from view. I did this in my single life and continued it in my marriage. When I experienced struggles, I worked to resolve them as best I could on my own because I didn't want anyone to think I was not okay. This allowed my addiction to take deeper root while avoiding detection for years. If my wife and I were in conflict or if either of us was having trouble individually, I still portrayed us as doing fine. Even in weekly therapy, I downplayed anything that related to my compulsive sexuality and I justified my actions if they came to light. There were aspects of my addiction that I wore as a badge of honor to denote my edgy and outsider status, but I usually showed these only to those I hoped would be impressed. I might also hint at these things as a way to put out bait for people with whom I might act out, but for the most part I kept anything hidden that I thought might give away the depth of my actions and their compulsive nature.

I also subscribed to my family's belief that only one person was allowed to get angry, but that person was now me. I tried to keep my anger hidden most of the time, and then would have outbursts that neither I nor my family would see coming. I also felt threatened if my wife or daughter got angry, so I was likely to either go back to childhood patterns of trying to placate and manage their emotions, or I would ramp my own anger up to take control.

I was self-conscious about all this, so I tried to get my wife and daughter to join me in maintaining a shiny family image. This helped perpetuate the family culture of secrecy and denial. As with my family of origin, this family culture created fertile ground in which addiction could flourish. Even when everyone could see that something was wrong, I cheerfully maintained that everything was just fine as long as things went my way and enabled my addiction.

Recovery allowed us to find healthier ways to communicate not only with each other, something my wife and I had worked on for years, but also to communicate more honestly with the world. I started slowly letting the people closest to us know that we were not always happy and that I was not the model husband I tried so hard to portray. I worked on my anger and on allowing everyone in the family space to feel and express all of their emotions. Make no mistake, these changes were not instantaneous and they were not easy. Nevertheless, as we started into recovery, we unknowingly started into a new phase of open, honest communication. As with so many gifts in recovery, we did not see this coming but it arrived nonetheless.

Communication Styles

If you want to find healthier patterns for you and your family, it will be helpful to understand more about communication styles and how they show up in your life. While there are different variations on this theory, I find the following four styles nicely encapsulate what I see around addiction: Aggressive, Passive, Passive-Aggressive, and Assertive. I think of each style as a tool. Like all tools, each style has a purpose and thus can be helpful in the right circumstance, but if misapplied, can cause more harm than good. Let's look at each one and see what it has to offer.

Aggressive communication tends to be pushy or dominating. As with most of the communication styles, it is used for a person to get their way either in a specific situation or more broadly in a relationship, in this case by obviously trying to win. It thus often features a louder or more forceful tone of voice as well as tense body language and facial expressions, but may sound calm while talking faster or talking over other people. It may involve blaming others and pointing out their faults as a way to take power in the discussion or relationship. Aggressive communication often involves speaking in extremes, such as, "you always..." and "you never..." It may include simply talking until the other person gives in. It is most associated with anger, which often masks fear. This anger is often driven by the thought, "I must get my way," while the fear underneath it typically says, "If I don't win, things will be awful." These emotions and thoughts may be unconscious, but they are nonetheless powerful motivators.

Growing up, I witnessed the Aggressive style routinely from my dad. For him, it seemed to be a way to maintain discipline and order in the house, but it was also used to deal with any perceived interpersonal threats. Thus, if he was offended or felt disrespected in any way by almost anyone, he would unleash his anger and belittle them. I felt embarrassed by this as I moved into adolescence and saw him go after gas station attendants, hotel clerks, my mom, or anyone else he saw as having less power than him. Despite my judgment of this growing up, as an adult, I was prone to sudden outbursts of aggressive communication when I felt scared. I could not predict when this would happen, and I was often immediately remorseful. Still, I could not deny that this style was in my toolbox whether I wanted it there or not.

Such a stance may be unpleasant to be around, but it has its place. The Aggressive style is appropriate in crises where safety is on the line. In such situations, someone may have to take command and issue orders while those around them must obey. Through this, everyone's safety may be preserved. Military personnel sometimes use the Aggressive style, especially in life-or-death situations. When the bullets are flying, there is no time to gather everyone together and form a consensus. Instead, those in command must maintain control without worrying if anyone's feelings get hurt. While other crises may be less dire, the Aggressive style may be found in political debates, corporate boardrooms, or in any other situation where a lot of power or money is on the line, and especially when time is of the essence.

People who become accustomed to aggressive communication at work or on deployment often struggle when they come home and find that this style does not go over well with the people they love. If this is your go-to style, keep in mind that Aggressive communication is not meant to build relationships, it is meant for a short-term crisis. After the immediate threat is over, it can be traded in for a more situation-appropriate style.

As a family member, you may have encountered the Aggressive style if you ever challenged someone's active addiction. A suggestion that your loved one should cut back or stop their addictive activity could be met with anger, defensiveness, and personal attacks. Perhaps you heard something like, "My problem?!? What about you?!? Leave me alone!!!"

The explanation for this behavior is simple. If you threaten someone's addiction before they are ready to change, they may feel like you are threatening their life. Thus, whether consciously or not, your loved one will see it as a potential crisis and react accordingly. Awareness of this does not excuse such behavior but gives you a chance to avoid taking the outbursts personally. Even if your loved one is trying to make it personal, it isn't about you; it's about them trying to protect their addiction because they are terrified to be without it.

You may have also found yourself using aggressive communication when dealing with your loved one's addiction. While it may be understandable if you try to force a solution when you are scared for your loved one, you would do well to observe whether this style is really getting you what you want. Many family members have protested that active addiction is a crisis, so aggressive communication is appropriate. This sounds good in theory, but you are likely reacting to your fear of losing your loved one in the future rather than dealing with whatever is actually happening in the present.

Instead of this, consider openly expressing your fears to them and then letting go of the results. If you could order your loved one around to keep them safe and prevent negative outcomes, you wouldn't be reading this book. In trying to control what it not yours to control, you will likely be driving a wedge in your relationship and creating resentment while not actually solving any problems.

If you find yourself turning to aggressive communication as a matter of habit, what can you do? Relaxing your body language and reducing volume or tension in your voice will be a good starting point. Take time to listen to others without formulating your response while they're still talking. Avoid using absolutes like "always" and "never."

The most helpful thing is to recognize your underlying motivations, especially any fears. For instance, if you are constantly afraid that your loved one will not be okay unless you force or convince them to do the right thing, then you will stay locked into this style. This will remain true even if you see that it's neither getting you what you want nor bringing peace of mind to anyone involved. Once you recognize an underlying fear, try to resolve it in a way that doesn't rely on others behaving properly. You might try counseling, prayer, attending recovery fellowship meetings, or any combination of these things.

If you have been using the Aggressive style for as long as you can remember, you may have to dig deeper to find where the fears and habits come from. This effort will pay off much better than spending the same amount of time attempting to control the people around you while pushing them away emotionally. You can also see whether the things you are trying to say can be expressed in a more effective way. Note that "more effective" does not mean "gets others to do what I want." That does not really exist. "More effective" means that you are communicating better and building relationships. This involves being a safer person with whom to talk. Aggressive communication rarely feels safe to the recipients.

Sometimes when people are faced with, or grow up around, the Aggressive style, they meet it with aggressive communication of their own. Other times, people react with the opposite: the Passive style.

Passive communication goes along to get along. Passive communication is less obviously manipulative, but it is used just as surely for a person to get their way either in a specific situation or more broadly in a relationship. Instead of pushing to win, however, passive communication tries to keep the peace and avoid conflict or disapproval. This is often done through a quiet or meek tone and body language, but sometimes with false cheer or nonchalance. Passive communication can involve simply not speaking up at all. Passive communication is more likely to accept blame or be appeasing. It may involve ideas such as, "I'm okay with whatever you want," or, "You're right." While these could be honest expressions in some circumstances, the Passive style relies on them as a matter of course.

As an example, if you've ever known or been someone who always says they "don't care where we go for dinner," then you are probably dealing with passive communication. After all, everyone has some preference about what they like to eat. To consistently say otherwise is to lapse into dishonesty, usually to please others. This is a relatively benign example, but it illustrates a broader pattern in relationships, in which a person pretends to have little or no opinion in order to get what they really want: perceived security and safety.

Unfortunately, this sense of safety comes at a steep price. Relying on the Passive style can leave a person with little say in their lives, lowered self-esteem, and resentment if others do not respond in the way that the passive communicator wanted. Because it is inherently dishonest, it undermines open communication and thus does not help build healthy relationships. In families that struggle with addiction, passive communication can keep people from speaking up when they see something wrong.

In my adoptive family, my mother personified the Passive style. It was taken for granted that my father was the authority and had the final word. My mom acquiesced to his wishes and demands. My dad saw himself as a benign dictator who looked out for his family, and there was no doubt that my mom would give in whenever there was a disagreement. I watched this take a toll on my mom, especially when her passive communication could not guarantee peace.

This particularly came up when my dad was drinking, which led to the few outright fights I can recall. My mom challenged his getting drunk during family holidays and she was berated for it, including calling her vulgar names and telling her that she was nothing without him. She had chosen for years to always give in and pretend that she was okay with whatever he chose, so it was very hard for her to stand up for herself or the kids when things became intolerable. She would inevitably back down and then feel helpless and despairing. The safety and security she craved did not ultimately materialize from going along with someone else's opinions and wishes all the time, especially someone in the grip of addiction.

The Passive style nonetheless has its place. Many people use it selectively, such as when talking to a boss or a teacher. Like aggressive communication, passive communication is well-suited for a crisis, especially if the person using the Passive style would do best to follow others' commands. It works especially well in situations where the other person seems dangerous and has the upper hand, such as if you find yourself being held hostage.

Unfortunately, living with someone in their active addiction sometimes feels like a hostage crisis, as the addiction hijacks the family dynamic. It can be tempting to turn to passive communication to mollify them, especially if they obviously act out more in their addiction when upset. Family members may find themselves using the Passive style in hopes that this will not only keep the peace, but also reduce the addiction. Unfortunately, it is more likely to encourage the person with the addiction to keep going, knowing they can get family members to back down rather than set and keep boundaries.

Passive communication is not limited to family members. The person with the addiction may turn to this style not only as a way to get along in general, but also because it allows them to fly under the radar with their gambling, romancing, shopping, eating, drug use, etc. They always seem to give in and agree with others' suggestions, but then quietly go about their addictive acting out anyway. This particularly comes up when more than one family member acts compulsively. An unspoken deal can be struck in which they remain silent about each other's compulsive behavior and thus go unchallenged in their own addiction.

If you find that the Passive style has become your go-to, you might consider trying a few of the following tips. In some relationships, simply letting your voice and opinion be heard is a good start. This is easier if the people around you

189

are supportive, but you may not be so lucky. If they are uncomfortable or even upset with the changes, it may take more work to establish an assertive place in the relationship. The good news is that if you stick with the changes, others will eventually adjust. Notice times when you are tempted to give in and to pretend you are okay with it. Start to recognize patterns in this tendency. Does it come up more with certain people? How much do you do it with the addicted people in your life? What do you hope will come of this? How has that worked out so far? Answering these questions as honestly as possible will give you greater insight that can help you break these patterns. You might also consider that some conflict is healthy in relationships. While it may be uncomfortable, it is a sign that you are all being honest.

If passive communication is a lifelong habit, deeper work may be required. This will likely involve confronting the source of old fears around conflict. It will mean raising your self-esteem and what you see as your place in the world. It will certainly involve facing whatever fears and negative messages you carry regarding conflict. I recommend doing all this with a counselor who is skilled in dealing with such issues, although self-reflection and written work in recovery fellowships can also play a valuable role.

There is communication style that seeks to find a middle ground between the Aggressive and Passive styles. It is thus named for both: the Passive-Aggressive style.

Passive-Aggressive communication is an attempt for a person to get their way, like aggressive communication, but not get caught or confronted, like passive communication. This style often sows confusion because it sends mixed messages. This may happen through a sarcastic tone, quiet cutting comments, veiled accusations, jokes that seem a little insulting, mumbled complaints, comments made as the person is leaving the room, and communication where the tone and body language say something very different than the words used. It may show up without words at all, such as when a person stomps around the house or starts slamming cupboard doors instead of letting others know in a straightforward way that they are upset. It could look like sulking or pouting instead of openly expressing that they feel sad or hurt. The person using the Passive-Aggressive style will often deny it if confronted. If asked why they are upset, they may say, "You know why," or, "You obviously don't care, so why should I tell you." If asked what they were mumbling under their breath, then may say, "Nothing." That's what I always did.

I used aggressive and passive communication at times, but I took the Passive-Aggressive style on as my own as I moved into adolescence, and I still have to be careful that it does not show up in my communication. If I was upset with someone in my family or friend group, I wouldn't let them know in any clear way. Instead, I would start cracking little jokes that I knew would target a soft spot for them. I might say angry things quietly and then deny it or lie about what I had said. I was not trying to be convincing in this denial, I was trying to avoid getting caught while still leaving the other person hurt and uncertain. This is an important point about the Passive-Aggressive style: it is meant to keep the other people off balance and confused, even if the person using this style tells themselves they are the real victim around here. My sense of humor was based on making other people uncomfortable and coating everything in a thick layer of sarcasm.

A communication style that is based in misdirection and creating uncertainty fit perfectly with my addiction. After all, I was always trying to get away with things while maintaining plausible deniability. I could push boundaries and claim I was only joking. I could always leave 'em guessing, which meant that people could never really tell what I was up to. At least, that's what I hoped. Most of all, I was always being slyly dishonest, something that formed a cornerstone of both the Passive-Aggressive style and my addiction.

Many family members have found themselves turning to passive-aggressive communication. They may have grown up with this or they may have discovered it as a coping mechanism around a loved one's addiction, but either way it has become part of the repertoire. It can be tempting to turn to sarcasm or misdirection when facing the helplessness of watching someone you love circle the drain. This is especially true if they don't seem to want a better life, or don't want it enough to do what you think they should do. If it doesn't feel safe or worthwhile to be straightforward and honest but you can't stand being passive about it either, then the Passive-Aggressive style may seem like all that's left.

Happily, this is not true. There is one more option: the Assertive style. This is the one that turns out to be the most effective most of the time and also happens to be the most honest.

Notice that the three preceding styles are all attempts to feel safe through manipulation and dishonesty. The Aggressive style seeks safety through dominance, Passive through acquiescence, and Passive-Aggressive through pretending to acquiesce and then scoring points without getting caught.

In contrast to this, the Assertive style is based in openness and honesty. It is associated with greater serenity and courage. Assertive communication often features a calm tone and open body language. Someone engaging in assertive communication does not insist on getting their way, but is instead willing to hear all sides and find a path forward. This does not mean that core values ever have to be sacrificed or compromised, only that when boundaries need to be set, this is done in a clear and open manner, and when negotiation is more appropriate, it is also done in a straightforward way.

The Assertive style carries an underlying message, just like the other styles, but this one is not based in fear. The Aggressive style says, "I must get my way or it will be a disaster." The Passive style says, "I must not push for my way or it will be a disaster." And the Passive-Aggressive style says, "I must not get caught trying to get my way or it will be a disaster." In contrast to these, the Assertive style says, "I can ask for my way, stand up for my values, and be okay no matter what." In most situations in life, this is the most realistic view.

Some family members argue that this is not true when it comes to their loved one's recovery. They insist that they cannot be okay if their loved one is not doing well. While this is an understandable fear, human experience has shown otherwise. Many people have learned to be okay with outcomes they didn't think they could withstand. As the Al-Anon program says, members find serenity and even happiness whether their loved one gets sober or not.

Perhaps the continued addiction is not your worst fear. That may be reserved for the death of your loved one. This is very understandable, but living in such fear and letting it warp your communication style will not prevent the dreaded outcome. Instead, it will only get in the way of the relationship. Since none of us has the power of life and death, and thus we don't how long we have together, let us not waste whatever time we have on trying to manipulate each other through misuse of communication styles.

Communication does not need to be about getting others to do what you want. It can be about showing love and increasing connection. To move toward that, try staying open and honest and then letting go of the outcomes as much as possible.

Here are some tips:

1. *Use "I" statements.* This means talking from your own point of view. Starting the sentence with "I" rather than "You" or "We" makes the communication more personal and easier for the other person to hear. This is more than a simple grammar trick. It often allows the speaker to be more in touch with their emotions and message. If you switch pronouns and say "you" when you really mean "I," it has the opposite effect. Instead of feeling personal, it sounds as though you are telling someone else what their experience is or will be. This may feel safer to you because you don't have to deal with your own feelings as much, but it will feel less safe to others and they will have a harder time connecting to what you are trying to convey. Starting with "you" can also lead to saying things like, "You always," "You never," and talking down to others.

2. *Talk about your emotions.* Everything you say doesn't have to be laden with feeling but being able to name and describe your emotions conveys important information. This can help you connect and makes your motivations clearer. This often creates a feeling of greater safety for the other person, which in turn makes it easier for them to open up as well. All too often, we say "I feel," but then follow this with what we think instead, such as saying, "I feel like you need to get a job." The problem is, "you need to get a job," is not a feeling. It is a thought. Instead, you might try saying, "I feel scared when I see you unemployed." This expresses the emotions you are feeling while also conveying what inspires those emotions. One way to catch if you are substituting thoughts for emotions is to notice that if the sentence starts with "I feel <u>like</u>" then it will probably name only name thoughts. Instead, say, "I feel" and then name your emotions using only a few words, like "happy," "sad," etc.

3. *Use reflective listening.* This involves putting the other person's main points into your own words and then checking with them to see if you got it right. This leads to one of two outcomes. Either they can confirm that you got their meaning and then you both know they were properly understood, or they have the opportunity to correct any misinterpretation. Either

outcome tends to create greater understanding and connection while ensuring better communication in general. You don't have to reflect back everything someone says to you, but it can be very helpful for the important points in a conversation or any time you are not certain that you are fully comprehending what it being said.

4. *Don't keep bringing up the past.* This is an Al-Anon slogan that fits well with assertive communication. It doesn't mean that you can never reference anything that has happened before or that your previous hurts must go ignored. It means that if you find yourself constantly giving "history lessons," especially about others' behavior, then you are likely trying to get them to feel and behave the way you want. In other words, constantly bringing up the past is a form of manipulation.

5. *Don't tell other people what they think and feel.* Mind reading belongs on a carnival boardwalk and not in a family relationship, so instead of telling someone else what they are thinking and feeling, ask them. You might be tempted to ask, "Are you feeling (angry/sad/happy)?" It is better to ask a completely open question, such as, "How are you feeling about this?"

6. *Maintain eye contact.* This does not mean staring the other person down. Instead, just make sure you are looking the other person in the eyes most of the time. This conveys interest and respect while giving both of you the opportunity to catch all the subtleties of emotion and meaning that the eyes convey.

7. *Remember that you can be okay no matter what.* This can be a tough one to swallow sometimes, but it makes assertive communication much, much easier. This is because such an attitude takes fear out of the conversation, allowing you to focus on being open and honest rather than pushing to get your way. If you are in a negotiation, this understanding will give you a stronger position because you can walk away if need be. You can also stand up for what is most important to you without undercutting yourself with worry that the other person won't like you as much. Spirituality both in and out of the recovery fellowships can help with this, because if you believe there is a higher power with a perfect plan for you and/or your loved one, then it's a lot easier to let go and communicate in a more straightforward way.

Don't worry if you don't do all these things or don't do them perfectly right off the bat. If the family has a multigenerational pattern of addiction, assertive communication may have been in short supply. You may try out one of the tips until it feels more natural, then add another one, then another. Be patient with yourself and see what this style can do for you.

As it turns out, the Assertive style can do more than just help with communication in the family. It is also the basis of both effective feedback and effective boundaries, which will be the subjects of the next two sections.

Effective Feedback

Many family members tell me they are afraid they will say the wrong thing to their loved one and screw everything up. Alternatively, some family members seem all too eager to give lectures and advice in hopes of talking their loved one into sobriety. Neither approach makes for effective communication or feedback. Let's look at what might work better.

First and foremost, I've found that feedback works best if the person at the receiving end is open to it. Don't bother giving a bunch of feedback to someone who doesn't want to hear it, no matter how much you think you have the magic words that they desperately need to hear.

How can you tell if they are open?

Ask.

The simplest form of this is, "Are you open to feedback?" Variations include, "Would you like to hear my opinion,"

"Are you open to my point of view," or, "May I offer my thoughts?"

Next, pause long enough for them to give an honest answer before you go charging in with what you wanted to say. If they say no, you may feel frustrated or disappointed, but it's actually a golden opportunity to build the relationship. This is because relationships and communication are built on safety and trust. If people feel safe and trusting, they will naturally move into closer relationship. If they feel unsafe or untrusting, they will push away.

If you can respect their wishes by not giving unwelcome feedback, you are showing them that you are a safe and trustworthy person in your communication. They may even come around a few minutes later and say that they are open after all. Receiving feedback can feel very vulnerable so people want to know they are safe before opening themselves up to hear potential criticism or attack.

Another way to build trust is to ask for feedback from them. This moves away from the top-down model in which your life looks pretty good and theirs looks pretty bad, so you are going to talk down to them from on high. I don't know about you, but I am less open to hearing someone's thoughts if they seem to be talking down to me. Asking for feedback indicates that you understand that no one has all the answers for anyone else's life, but that you respect them enough to hear their point of view. It also says that you want to move toward a more equal relationship.

If they say they are open to your feedback, here are some ideas to help things go more smoothly. You may notice that many of these are drawn directly from the Assertive communication style.

- *Use "I" statements* – This is particularly important in giving feedback because it promotes humility rather than talking down to your loved one, and it acknowledges that your opinion is just that: an opinion. Using "I" statements allows your loved one to take what they like and leave the rest.

- *Check your motives* – Are you trying to talk them into your point of view? They didn't ask for that and it probably isn't welcome.

- *Keep it short and sweet* – Get in, give your perspective, and then get back out. If you find yourself "looping," that is to say repeating the same ideas or talking points over and over again, you are probably trying to convince them to do what you want. That's manipulation, not feedback.

- *Stick to the subject at hand* - They agreed to hear feedback, not a primer on everything they are doing wrong.

- *Avoid giving lectures and advice* – If you could lecture and advise them better, it would have happened by now.

- *Don't tell them what they think and feel* – Instead, tell them what you think and feel.
- *When you say, "I feel," follow it with an emotion word* – Too often, we say, "I feel" and then tell people what we think instead. For instance, we might say, "I feel like you need to get a job." As noted in the previous section, "you need to get a job" is not a feeling. Try saying something like, "I feel scared when I see you are unemployed" instead. You can usually tell when you are describing feelings because they are summed up in one or two words, such a "happy," "sad," or "frustrated."
- *Be vulnerable* – This is the essence of effective feedback. It is vulnerable to tell someone else how you felt when seeing them in a certain state or after an action. This may be expressed in statements such as, "When you got drunk again, I felt scared and angry. I feel happy that we can talk about it now, and cautiously optimistic about the future."
- *Look for points of relation rather than differences* – When we ask someone to get sober, we are asking them to do one of the scariest things they have ever done. Think of a time when you faced your greatest fears, or what it might feel like to give up your most trusted coping skills for the rest of your life. Find empathy and how you can relate to what your loved one is going

through, rather than thinking, "I don't have an addiction so I have no idea why they don't just stop."

- *Let go of the result* – This may be the most important point of all. You have no control over how they take your feedback or what they do in response. This will be true no matter how many times or ways you say it. Constantly trying to get them to do what you want will only impede the relationship. Instead, give your best feedback and then get out of the way.

Effective Boundaries

Many family members tell me they struggle with setting and maintaining boundaries. While this is often true, many people start by misunderstanding what a boundary even looks like. Family members often think of boundaries as being rules that are laid out for others to follow, such as, "You can't come over here drunk," or variations like, "Please don't come over here drunk." I understand why such statements could be thought of as boundaries, but there is a fatal weakness in this model. Simply put, most people aren't sure what to do if the other person doesn't follow the rule. This leads family members to tell me that there is no point in setting boundaries with their addicted loved one because that person does whatever they want anyway.

Thus, we see that the statement, "You can't come over here drunk" is not really a boundary. Instead, it is an expression of hope, one that is likely doomed to failure if you are dealing with someone who is highly motivated to keep getting drunk. For this reason, I refer to statements such as this as "requests for change," not boundaries. A request for change can be an appropriate first action but does not guarantee anything will happen differently than before. To get a new outcome, an effective boundary needs to be set.

Effective boundaries are, at their heart, "if/then" statements that express how you will change your behavior in response to what someone else does. For instance, rather than saying, "You can't come over here drunk," you might say, "If you come over here drunk, I will ask you to leave. If you refuse to leave, I will call the police."

Note that neither of these statements tells the other person what to do. Instead, they tell that person what *you* will do. This acknowledges that the other person has freedom of choice about how they will proceed, while giving them fair warning about what to expect if they take certain actions.

Some people see these statements as ultimatums, but this is only true if your boundaries warn of unrealistically disastrous consequences for not complying, such as, "If you come over here drunk, I will never speak to you again." I call this "leading with the nuclear option" and it is only appropriate if you have truly reached your limit and are willing to follow through with the threatened consequence. Checking with yourself first to determine your most realistic response will pay dividends. It helps you set boundaries that are not empty threats and it keeps you from painting yourself into a corner by saying you will do something you do not wish to do.

You may feel drawn to lead with the nuclear option if you think it will change the other person's behavior, but keep in mind that this provides only the illusion of control. In reality, the other person is going to choose their responses and actions no matter what you threaten. Trying to manage and control them through dramatic and unrealistic boundaries is actually an attempt at manipulation. Tempting as this may be, it will not lead to healthy relationships nor will it provide the sense of safety and security that it promises.

Boundaries need not be expressed only as negative consequences to undesirable actions. Instead, they can describe the positive outcomes for desired behavior. Our basic boundary might first be expressed as, "If you are sober, I'd be happy to have you over." Such boundaries are set all the time in everyday situations, such as, "If you get good grades, I'll pay for you to go to college," or, "If you do a good job, there's a bonus in it for you." Try to think of how your boundaries might be phrased as positive or affirmative statements.

Once people understand how to set effective boundaries, they are faced with the next step: figuring out where to set those boundaries. I have two simple guidelines on this. The first is to set boundaries that protect your safety and the safety of those you love to the best of your ability. For instance, you might set boundaries around not allowing drug use or violent behavior in your home. The second guideline is to set boundaries that stand up for your values. This could include boundaries that stand up for honesty, fairness, teamwork, etc.

Let's look at some examples. If you want to protect the safety of yourself and your home, you might say, "If you become violent in my home, I will call the authorities and I won't bail you out if you are arrested as a result." If your safety and that of those you love seems threatened by someone's drug use, you can speak to that as well. If you want to set a boundary standing up for an important value, it might sound like, "If you are able to show up in a spirit of teamwork and fully participate, we would love to include you in more family events. If not, we understand and will include you less often."

As a personal example, when I took a girlfriend (who later became my wife) to meet my family for the first time, I called my dad ahead of time. I told him, "If you start drinking while she is there, we will get in the car and leave immediately." I had not dared to say anything like this to my father before, but I knew how important the safety of my new relationship was to me. He became upset and asked how I could even think he would do such a thing, seeming to forget that he had once swung at me in front of a previous girlfriend when he was drunk. I didn't argue with him or try to convince him of my point of view; I just restated the boundary. I never saw him take a drink of alcohol again, even though he didn't stop using it until about 20 years after that. Your mileage may vary, but it is undeniable that setting this boundary changed our relationship for the better.

Once you know what boundaries you want to set and you have expressed them clearly, the next step is to maintain and enforce them. This is vital, because a boundary is only as effective as your follow-through. As much as you might hope that setting a boundary will be met with respect, the other person may be perfectly happy to maintain the status quo. In fact, it is our natural tendency as human beings to try to keep social relationships the way they are, even if we don't like the way they are. Thus, if you set new boundaries, people may test them just to see if they can get you to go back to your old ways. They may not even realize they are doing so, but the effort is real nonetheless.

Because of all of this, it is up to you to make change happen. This sounds simple in principle, right? Just do what you said you were going to do. Unfortunately, simple is not the same as easy. Let's look at common difficulties in keeping boundaries, and how you can maintain them anyway.

The factor that I see most frequently undermining otherwise good boundaries is fear of conflict. If you are afraid to be in conflict with the person at the receiving end of a boundary, they can get you to back down by threatening conflict when you try to enforce that boundary. This could look like raising their voice, using a hostile tone and body language, or making overt threats. Sometimes they don't even need to do that much. They might just give you a look. Finally, you may undermine your own boundaries without any contribution from them. Perhaps as you are talking, you start to anticipate conflict and back down or start to compromise without them doing a thing.

Keep in mind that the other person has no power to change your behavior any more than you have the power to change theirs. Therefore, it's not their fault if you don't keep your boundary. You're the one who makes the decision to back down, or not.

Another common thing that undermines boundaries is fear that the other person won't like you as much if you change your behavior and stand up for yourself. This fear does not require them to be hostile. They may act hurt or confused by your new attitude and actions. They may convey this through verbal or nonverbal means. Once again, you may back down because of this fear without any contribution on their part.

Yet another way to undermine your boundaries is by feeling guilty for standing up for yourself. You may decide it is selfish to advocate for yourself, but this is unlikely to be true. Selfishness involves not caring if anyone else is hurt or deprived as you do what you want. Rather than that, we are talking about making sure you are okay before doing the same for those around you. This is akin to the familiar analogy of putting your oxygen mask on before trying to help someone else. The reality is that most family members reading this book will not have any real struggle with selfishness on their own part, but if they are dealing with someone who has an active addiction, they are likely to struggle with that person being selfish, because addiction is selfish by nature.

To summarize, don't try to set boundaries by telling others what they can and can't do; instead tell them what you are going to do. Set your boundaries in order to protect your safety and stand up for your values rather than trying set boundaries that get others to change. Once your boundaries are set, stand by them.

Chapter 6

Codependency

Codependency is a concept that does not have a clear definition, yet still has utility in helping people. You can't get diagnosed with codependency by a mental health professional, but you can find treatment for it offered in residential settings, intensive workshops, and outpatient counseling. There are many books about codependency, and the 12 Step group Codependents Anonymous [CoDA] is dedicated to recovery from it[1], yet the definition of codependency can vary among all of these. Some people even argue that the idea is so broadly applied that it can be harmful.[2] Nonetheless, it is hard to be a family member of someone with an addiction and not run into the concept of codependency. It thus merits discussion to see where this idea came from, some common definitions, if and how it may show up in your life, and what to do about it if it does.

The idea of codependency is traced by some theorists back to the 19th Century, but the modern conceptualization started to gain professional attention in the 1940's and 50's. Theorists pointed out patterns of thoughts, feelings, and behaviors in the family members of people with alcohol addiction. According to one research survey, broad patterns described included "a dysfunctional pattern of relating to others with an extreme focus outside of oneself, a lack of emotional expression, and personal meaning derived from relationships with others."[3] This was taken to be a result of living with someone who was addicted, and was thought to be most pronounced in those who grew up with it. The term "codependent" came from this assumption. The idea was that the person with the addiction was dependent on alcohol while their spouse and other family members played a complimentary role in this dependence by putting up with it or even making it easier, thus being "co-dependent."

This idea has been criticized as blaming the family and even pathologizing traits traditionally associated with and encouraged in women, such as being supportive and selfless.[2] Arguably, such traits were necessary survival mechanisms for women who were effectively trapped in marriages to men who were addicted, especially in times when women had few options to support themselves or leave their husbands. Children raised in such an environment were even more trapped unless a relative or social service pulled them out, which could still feel traumatic.

Despite these criticisms, the idea of codependency caught on and then gained popularity in the late 20th and early 21st centuries, with interest and research seeming to peak in the 1980's and 90's.[3] During this time, the concept of codependency captured the popular imagination, fueled in part by such books as the seminal *Codependent No More* by Melody Beattie. In the process of this happening, the definition began to expand beyond the world of chemical dependency and changed into the idea that the traits of codependency might show up in people who had even moderately dysfunctional families, regardless of whether there was any chemical dependency present.[1] This blurring of the definition welcomed more people into recovery from codependency but also invited backlash, as professionals and laypeople alike started to question whether this was just a catchall term for anyone with relationship or connection issues.

Nonetheless, the idea of codependency still proves helpful to many family members when it is used in its original meaning: how attitudes, behaviors, and feelings can be shaped by living with addiction. When viewed in this context, family members benefit from recognizing the signs of codependency in their own lives and can then work to change these tendencies.

The biggest hallmark of codependency is that the codependent person seems to be addicted to or psychologically dependent on the person with the more obvious addiction to a substance or destructive behavior.

You might think, "Well, that's not me! I'm not dependent on my kid (or lover, parent, etc.)." But is this true? If you feel like you can't be okay unless they are okay, that is a form of psychological dependence. This is starkly illustrated if you struggle whenever they struggle, or even struggle because you think they may struggle in the future. If this describes you, then you have become psychologically dependent on them to be okay.

As a result, you might go to extraordinary lengths to try to keep them from struggling. Someone once told me, "They had their arms wrapped around the bottle, and I had my arms wrapped around them." While this looks to some like love, and you may have been raised to think this is what love is, it is really an attempt to avoid your own suffering. In fact, to avoid that suffering, you may find yourself doing many of the same things people with addictions do. Let's look at a few examples.

People with addictions are often manipulative to get their fix. People who are codependent may also become manipulative with their loved one in an effort to get them to be okay. This could include saying things they don't mean or pretending to feel some way they don't really feel, all in hopes that they will get the addicted person to stop acting out.

People with addictions often minimize their behavior or the consequences of it, saying their addictive actions are not that bad, could be worse, are no big deal, are not as bad as someone else's, etc. Codependent people can also minimize, either downplaying their own outlandish efforts to get someone else sober, or else minimizing how badly the addicted person is doing. This could involve downplaying the severity of the situation to themselves just as much as they may downplay things to everyone else, often with the justification that, "I don't want people to see my loved one in a bad light." Rather than protecting your loved one, however, you mostly end up protecting the addiction.

People with addictions often rationalize and justify their actions. This is usually in an effort to get others to support or at least back off of the addictive acting out, but sometimes it is done to keep power in a relationship. Codependence can also lead you to rationalize and justify. This may take the form of rationalizing and justifying your own actions, such as saying, "I had to do what I did to save them," or it might involve rationalizing and justifying the actions of the person with the addiction, such as saying, "It's okay that they keep using, because of what they have gone through." Sometimes, the deeper rationalization is done internally, through making up reasons why you do what you do or they do what they do, all in an effort to avoid feeling the potentially painful emotions involved in facing the truth around addiction.

One more example would be that people with addictions develop a tolerance, which demands that more of the drug or behavior is needed in order to get the desired feeling. In the same way, you as a family member can develop a tolerance in the sense of putting up with more and more of the addictive behavior in your loved one or getting so used to awful behavior that previously intolerable actions are now accepted. Tolerance can also develop in such a way that you demand more and more reassurance that your loved one is okay or that their behavior is heading in the direction you want. As a result, you may get to the point that you find yourself constantly checking up on them, tracking their location, monitoring their communications, asking them probing questions, etc.

Having read the examples above, consider how many of the following behaviors and attitudes you may have in common with your loved one in their addiction:

- Minimizing
- Rationalizing
- Justifying
- Keeping secrets
- Lying to cover addictive behavior
- Developing a tolerance
- Burying emotions
- Hiding motives
- Outbursts of anger
- Depressive episodes
- Health problems

- Stress
- Shame
- Guilt
- Escapism into video, food, shopping, work, exercise, etc.

No list could cover every possible similarity between the person with the addiction and the person who is codependent with them. Instead, use this as a starting point to see where you may be showing signs of codependency, and where you can find greater empathy for your loved one. In doing so, you create opportunities to move out of judgment and fear, and into solution.

Such solution may take many forms. Recovery fellowships and therapy are available around codependency. Among the recovery fellowships, Codependents Anonymous, also known as CoDA, would be the most obvious starting place. CoDA is a Twelve Step fellowship that encourages members to admit powerlessness over others, which is to say that members acknowledge that, without help, they can't stop trying to manipulate other people or relying on them for their wellbeing. Having admitted this, members then use the remaining eleven steps to get spiritual support and remove internal barriers so that they can live lives increasingly free from codependency. SMART Recovery does not use the term codependency, and some members vehemently oppose the term as unscientific, but the tools of SMART can be very helpful nonetheless. The SMART Recovery Family & Friends workbook has many science-based exercises and ideas that directly address some of the issues that fall under the codependency umbrella. Similarly, many people find they can use the meetings and tools of Al-Anon, Nar-Anon, and Families Anonymous to work on these same traits. Having the social support of recovery fellowship meetings is helpful to many family members trying to work on their codependency. For some it is absolutely necessary.

Therapy can also be helpful with codependency attitudes and behaviors. While not all therapists will think of or address these issues under the term "codependency," any therapist should be able to recognize that codependent behaviors and attitudes are unhealthy. Avoid any therapist who tells you to "just stop" for the same reasons you would avoid a professional who gave the same advice about a chemical addiction. Instead, seek the help of someone who understands the nature of compulsive behavior and can help address it. If you find your codependency traits and behaviors are severely impacting your life, you may consider seeking residential treatment. This is far more rare than drug addiction treatment and it may be difficult to get insurance to cover it, but it is available.

Chapter 7

Enabling vs. Helping

Aquestion that I often hear from family members is, "How can I tell if I am enabling or if I am helping?" When I first started working with families, I thought there might be a list of behaviors that were "enabling" and that my job would be to give families that list and help them to avoid those behaviors. As I grew in my understanding of recovery, I came to a different conclusion. I saw that enabling and helping are not two different categories of behavior, but are actually two different mindsets. If someone can shift their mindset, their behavior will likely change on its own rather than requiring them to constantly check an internal or external list of "right" or "wrong" actions. Some actions might fall into the category of "enabling" with one mindset while being "helping" in another. In this chapter, we'll look at the difference in mindset and what you can do to take on more helpful beliefs.

One of the major differences between a helpful mindset and an enabling mindset is that a helpful mindset is based on sticking to your values and being honest with yourself, whereas an enabling mindset is based in fear. One great way to keep yourself on track for a helpful mindset is to remember a popular recovery slogan: "To thine own self be true." This Shakespeare quote nicely sums up both ideas. In modern English, it implies that we must be true to our values and who we are. In the original Elizabethan English, it would mean to be honest with yourself. As we'll see throughout this chapter, living by these two concepts can make all the difference.

So, what makes for an enabling mindset? The underlying assumptions. One assumption is that you can keep someone else from their addiction or cause them to get worse. Another is that if you challenge the addiction, it will lead to conflict that you can't withstand. A third is that if you love someone, you should go along with what they want. A fourth is that, based on the previous assumptions, you should set your values aside and do things that you would not otherwise do.

You may not see yourself reflected in every one of those assumptions, but I challenge you to look as deeply as you can into your attitudes and behavior to see if any fit. Get feedback on this from someone who not only knows you but is also insightful and honest. Ideally, talk to a counselor or recovery fellowship member who is experienced with such issues, because any one of these assumptions by itself can lead to enabling and distress, and a combination of several will almost certainly do so.

The first assumption of enabling, that you can keep someone else from their addiction or cause them to get worse, is one of the most common misconceptions that family members carry. It has been covered in other parts of this book but bears a quick review because it can underpin much enabling behavior.

If you believe you can keep someone from their addiction, then you are likely to try to do so by doing things you would not otherwise do. This might include letting them live with you even though they pay no rent or can't be counted on to do so consistently. You might put up with messes around the house or behaviors that would get anyone else kicked out, such as being verbally abusive or stealing from you. Another example might be hiring them at the family business even though they produce so much less than any other employee, are constantly late or absent, or otherwise don't act like anyone you would have there. All of this might be done with the thought that if you ask them to leave, their addiction will get worse. Perhaps you tell yourself that they just need a change of scenery, that this will keep them from their old patterns. This could lead to planning an elaborate family vacation, one you're sure will bring the family together and help them see that there is a life better than addiction. You may then come to find that they have their own have plans for that trip, seeing it as a chance to indulge in their addiction with fewer of life's usual responsibilities and pressures.

Perhaps you go even further than planning a vacation, and instead think that you can solve their problems by giving them a fresh start in a new city. This may be their idea or yours, but unless they are already showing concrete actions of a new resolve in their recovery, their problems will likely follow them to their new address or be recreated there from scratch.

If you think you have the power to make their addiction worse, you will naturally try to avoid this. This may take the form of staying silent when you see things you don't approve of or even taking abuse, all out of fear that speaking up will worsen their addiction. Perhaps they have even told you that they would get better if you stopped bothering them about things. This silent enabling can wear at your soul, leave you feeling more and more helpless, reinforce itself by leading to more tolerance of intolerable behavior, and still make no improvement in their condition.

Likewise, if you believe you have the power to make their addiction worse, then you might be tempted to try to avoid this by giving them money or a place to stay even though you don't approve of anything they are doing with these things. You may give them access to your car or get them one of their own even though you know they may drive under the influence. Perhaps they have made promises that this will never happen again if you give them one more chance. They may even mean it with all their hearts, but you both may come to learn that this resolve will crumble if the addiction takes over. You may find your own resolve similarly crumbles if you tell yourself that you can make their addiction worse by withholding the money, the shelter, or the vehicle.

What if you withhold such things from your loved one and their condition does get worse? Doesn't that make it your fault? Tempting or scary as it may be to think so, it is simply not true. No matter how much you or your loved one believe you are the cause of their struggles, the reality is that they chart their own course. If that course does not include vigorous recovery efforts, then nothing you do or say will make any real difference.

Does this mean you should never offer any money or other assistance? Not necessarily. Instead, use "To thine own self be true" as your guide. Ask yourself if the money or other assistance is guaranteed to be used for something you believe in. For instance, I believe in counseling as an effective way to improve a situation. Therefore, I have no problem pulling out my wallet to pay for counseling for my daughter. You may feel the same way about bigger things like helping your loved one go to treatment, or smaller things such as giving them a ride to a recovery meeting. Remember that you have no obligation to help, and that doing these things is not guaranteed to make things better for your loved one, but you can rest your head on the pillow at night knowing that the actions you took matched your values. In the end, that is the best any of us can do.

The second assumption on our list is that if you challenge the addiction, it will lead to conflict you can't withstand. It's true that challenging someone's addiction will likely produce conflict. In fact, all relationships involve some conflict. This doesn't have to be awful and it doesn't have to be avoided. Problems come when you assume that conflict is something that you must dodge at all costs or that it will automatically make the situation worse. If you tend to avoid conflict in all relationships, it may be hard to challenge these assumptions, but challenge them you must. If you don't, then the addiction is likely to win more of the time, because your loved one only needs to push that button to get you to back off. This allows them to continue their addiction while you feel helpless to do anything to stand up for yourself, your safety, and your values.

This means that you will have to find a way to break through the idea that conflict must be avoided. If this belief seems to apply mostly to your relationship with your loved one who has an addiction, then you may be able to change your belief through better information. Some people think they must avoid upsetting their loved one because their loved one seems to act out in their addiction more when upset. This is likely true, but if you are reading this book, chances are that your loved one acts out in their addiction no matter what mood they are in. They may even be using conflict and anger as excuses to use more. This shows that conflict is not really why they are using or acting out, and that if they don't have that excuse, they will likely find another. In fact, without some conflict or discomfort, your loved one will likely never change. You don't have to manufacture conflict to get them to change (remember you don't have that power) but you don't need to avoid it either.

If, on the other hand, you avoid conflict in most relationships, then this is a deeper issue that needs to be addressed not only for this relationship, but also for your overall safety and comfort in life. As mentioned earlier, all relationships include some conflict and disagreement. This does not have to mean fighting or ugliness. It does mean that you either learn to stand up for your safety and your values, or you are likely to live a life of anxiety and being manipulated by people who exploit this avoidance. Fear may push you to choose the avoidance anyway, but this fear is probably an exaggerated artifact from childhood. As with many such old beliefs, it likely does not fit your adult life as well as you think. Nonetheless, childhood beliefs are not easy to set aside, so most people need help to let them go. Such help may come through recovery fellowships or self-help books, but for many people there will be nothing speedier and more effective than individual therapy.

The third assumption is that if you love someone, you should go along with what they want. This may be rooted in the fear of conflict detailed above. In this case, you may hope that going along with your loved one's desires will avoid conflict. It may also come from a belief that your loved one should be happy at all times and that it is up to you to make this happen. At first blush, you may think this doesn't apply to you, but check your actions to see what tale they tell. Do you find yourself doing things to appease them if they seem unhappy? Do you feel uncomfortable when they seem uncomfortable? Do you try to "correct" this by doing things you don't really want to do? Do you try to talk them into feeling better by agreeing with them out loud even when you don't agree in your heart? Do you let them talk you into things that don't match your own values and desired outcomes? If you answered yes to one or more of these questions, you are falling for the third assumption.

If so, ask yourself what makes this seem like a good idea. Perhaps you fear that not going along with what they want will only make things worse. Note that this is based in the first two assumptions, because it implies that you can make things better or worse and that you should avoid the natural conflict of not agreeing to do what they want. Perhaps you were raised to think that giving someone whatever they want, whether possessions or permission, is a true expression of love. Whether this is true in most relationships is debatable, but when faced with a loved one in the grip of addiction, it can be deadly. It is arguably a much better expression of love to set and keep healthy boundaries, since people with active addiction are prone to wanting things that are patently self-destructive.

This all leads to the fourth assumption, that based on the first three assumptions, you should set your values aside and do things that you would not otherwise do. This is where "To thine own self be true" becomes a potent tool. If the first three assumptions of unhealthy enabling are followed, then you will likely find yourself doing things that don't match with your values and standards. This is the heart of unhealthy enabling. Thus, to move out of unhealthy enabling and into healthy helping, stick with actions that match your values and who you are as a person. If you can do this, then the first three assumptions won't cause you anywhere near as much trouble. They might leave you wanting to do things that will not work out well, but you are not going to follow through on those regrettable actions because you will only do things that you believe in.

As mentioned above, one of the best ways to stick to this standard is to be honest with yourself. This starts with being honest about what values are most important to you. We all hold several such values and they sometimes come into conflict with one another, or at least seem to do so. For instance, I may highly value keeping my family out of pain but also treasure honesty. When confronted with a situation in which I want to save my loved one from pain, I may be tempted to bend or even break the truth. I will then have to decide which value will win, because they don't seem compatible in that moment. If I decide honesty is the most important, I can still use my other value to guide me to being honest in the least painful way. If I decide that protecting them from pain is most important, I may use the other value to stay as honest as I can while keeping them from pain. Either way, I will regret my actions least when I make sure I am honoring my values and acknowledging which are held most dear.

Another way to be honest with yourself is to see where you may fall into old family enabling patterns rather than making decisions based on who you are. Such patterns may include trying to keep everyone happy and swooping in to rescue family members who don't seem as happy as we think they should be. Unfortunately, this can lead to family members not knowing how to tolerate distress in life without expecting to be rescued from it. Alternatively, they may learn to hide any unhappiness from you in order to keep you from the apparent distress of trying to keep them happy. This can become an endless cycle of caretaking each other, and it flies in the face of open, honest relationships.

To get out of this pattern, you may need to be honest in ways that are new for you. For instance, rather than rescuing your loved one, you might think to yourself or even say to them, "I am tempted to fall into my old pattern of trying to keep you happy all the time. Instead, I can be there for you as you go through your natural emotions." This is being honest with yourself and others about your motivations and temptations, while being true to who you are by honoring your willingness to change.

A second family enabling pattern is trying to protect family members from the natural consequences of their actions. This could range from something as simple as cleaning up after someone's drunken mess, all the way to paying endless legal bills to keep them from feeling the sting of their transgressions. Each time, you might say, "This is the last time I do this," or, "I hope you've learned your lesson." Unfortunately, the lesson they may learn is that someone will always save them from themselves. No matter how remorseful they may feel, their addiction will whisper in their ear that they can get away with it one more time since it's always worked out so far. If you choose to cut off the support, or at least the finances, keep in mind that they may find someone else to keep rescuing them, but at least you can take yourself out of that unhealthy role.

Getting out of this family pattern will involve being honest with yourself. To keep rescuing someone over and over relies on fooling yourself into thinking "this time will be the one that opens their eyes" when the evidence has shown you otherwise. This is understandable the first time your loved one gets into a scrape, but with each repetition, it takes more and more denial on your part, which is to say not being honest with yourself.

The third family enabling pattern is being willing to debate every decision. This pattern means you allow yourself to get drawn into back-and-forth debates over anything your loved one does not like, especially any of your thoughts or decisions that threaten their addictive status quo. They may argue a point until they find the angle that gets you to back down, or they may just debate until you give in out of frustration. Either way, their main objective is to keep you engaged in the argument, not to actually find the best idea.

Thus, your escape from this pattern is not to find better arguments in hopes they will change their mind, but instead to sidestep the entire pattern by not engaging in the debate. You can say, "I am not interested in arguing about this. I have made my point of view clear and it is not up for debate." Don't expect them to leave you alone right away. You may have to repeat those words several times. In fact, saying the same thing in response to anything they present is a clear message that they aren't going to draw you in again. You may have to stick to your guns for a while before they get frustrated and give up. They may resort to other tactics such as yelling at you, insulting you or calling you names, throwing a tantrum, or storming off to punish you. Stay the course and they will eventually come to the conclusion that you are not going in for the same old trap.

Notice that in all of these family enabling patterns, the solution is to be true to your values and honest with yourself and others. That can be hard, especially if you are not used to making decisions this way. This is one reason why enlisting help in your recovery is so important. Both trained professionals and people in recovery fellowships can offer perspectives you might not have considered. They can give opinions based in experience with the types of struggles you are facing, and bring perspective to the emotions many of us feel so strongly when it comes to making decisions that affect the people we love. They can also offer support as you try these new behaviors and ride out the initial discomfort, especially if your loved one tries various ways to push you back into your old behaviors.

To review, here are questions to ask yourself if you are uncertain whether you are about to head into unhealthy enabling or healthy helping.

"Is the action I'm considering true to my values?"

"Am I being honest with myself?"

"Am I doing this out of fear?"

"Am I honoring my own needs and feelings in making this decision?"

"Am I telling myself that if I do or don't do this, it will make my loved one's addiction better or worse?"

"If I'm feeling uncertain, have I gotten a second opinion from someone who has experience with such issues and decisions?"

Answer these questions as honestly as you can so that you can move out of unhealthy enabling, and into healthy helping.

Chapter 8

Family Dynamics and Roles

Social creatures that we are, our families are a vital part of how we define ourselves, whether we want them to be or not. The significance of family can be just as strong even if we rarely talk or are estranged from them. Given the level of influence family has over our lives, the dynamics in our family and the roles we play are worthy of our attention, especially once we see that we can start to change them if we are willing to put in the effort.

Family Dynamics

Every family has its own dynamic. In a healthy dynamic, roles are somewhat flexible and the family system can adapt to the normal changes of life. When a healthy family system is under stress, the roles can become temporarily more rigid but return to flexibility once the stress is removed. In an unhealthy family dynamic, the roles stay rigid and the family has trouble adapting.

Predictably, addiction thrives more in an unhealthy dynamic while simultaneously pushing that dynamic to be even less healthy, creating a tragic spiral. To make matters worse, family dynamics and roles are passed down from generation to generation, sometime explicitly, and sometimes by example and behavioral reinforcement. Luckily, these dynamics and roles are never set in stone, and with effort they can be changed and healed.

In this section, we will look at various family dynamics in order to give you the knowledge and tools you need to assess how these things may show up in your family. We will also see what you might do to improve your family's dynamics.

The term "family dynamics" refers to the overall pattern of how family members interact and relate to each other, as well as how the family functions as a whole. One common term around this is "functionality," with its most famous conjugation found in the idea of the "dysfunctional family." While this implies that a family is either functional or dysfunctional, there is actually a range, and every family falls somewhere along that range.

It should be noted that what is considered functional is somewhat culturally dependent. For instance, American families often expect their young adult children to move out of the house and start making their own way in the world. If they don't do this, some people might wonder what went wrong. In contrast, a friend from Italy was still living with her parents into her 40's because she hadn't gotten married. She explained that it would have been an insult to them to move out before marriage. In other words, if she had moved out, some people might have wondered what went wrong. Thus, if we say that a family is "too enmeshed," this must be taken in the context of the cultural norms of the society in which that family exists.

Having said that, let's see what sort of features are commonly considered functional or dysfunctional.

Functional families:

- Have clear rules and roles
- Engage in open, honest communication
- Balance the needs of the individual members with the needs of the whole family
- Allow outside input while maintaining family culture and traditions
- Can be flexible and adapt to change
- Balance consistency with new ideas
- Allow a full range of human emotions

Dysfunctional families:

- Have hidden rules and uncertain roles
- Engage in dishonest communication
- Have poor balance between the needs of the individual members and the needs of the whole family
- Are either closed to outside input or cannot maintain their own sense of identity
- Struggle to adapt to change

- Are overly rigid or chaotic
- Limit what emotions are acceptable

Keeping in mind that no family is completely functional or dysfunctional, consider how your family seems to be doing in each of these dimensions. You might rate the family on a scale of 0-10, with 0 being completely dysfunctional and 10 being completely functional. If you have helped create a family of your own, compare the functionality of your current family with that of the family in which you grew up. If there are significant differences in level of functionality, ask yourself why this is. Is it the product of deliberate choice or did it just seem to turn out that way?

We often don't like to look at luck as a factor, but it undeniably has an influence. We can see this when we recognize that family functionality can be impacted, sometimes profoundly, by the random events of life. An obvious example might be the sudden and unexpected death of one or more family members. A family that had been at one level of functionality may suddenly be thrust into disarray as a result, and then settle into a new level entirely. Chances are that this family will become less functional, at least in the short term, but it could become more functional instead. The difference might come down to which family traits become magnified, which family members were lost, what roles they played previously, which family members take up those roles moving forward, and what kind of outside support is available and accepted.

Hopefully, your family will not go through anything so extreme, but addiction often shows up as a strong and unpredictable factor in the functionality of a family, whether it goes off like a bombshell or creeps in slowly but surely. No matter how it enters the family system, addiction is likely to have a negative effect. Rules and roles may get clamped down or tossed out the window. Communication will suffer, because open, honest communication is hard to maintain around addiction, especially for the person who has the disease. Attention to needs will go out of balance as the person with addiction starts putting that need above all others, while other family members may be tempted to also pour more and more of the family resources into helping them recover. The family may start hiding the problem, which closes the family off from outside input more and more, or the family may lose or warp their sense of identity in the face of the onslaught of addictive troubles. The family may find they cannot adapt to the changes required. Some emotions, such as anger or sadness, may come to predominate, while others might be hidden or lost. This list is far from comprehensive, but it should serve to illustrate the point.

If the family has been dealing with addiction for generations, these problems intensify. This is because the changes described above likely happened decades ago and were then passed down from generation to generation until their source is forgotten, or perhaps deliberately buried. At a certain point, the dysfunctional patterns are taken for granted and occasionally even justified or made into points of pride ("That's just how our family is"). As these patterns become part of the family culture, they become harder and harder to change. Each new incidence of a family member becoming addicted only solidifies and entrenches the old family ways of coping with it.

This was the case in both my birth and adoptive families. On my birth mother's side, I know of addiction to alcohol and sex. My birth father's family included at least sex addiction. In my adoptive family, things are less clear, but my father had an addiction to alcohol, and it is rare that only one member out of the whole family tree will have such a struggle. Since addiction tends to include keeping secrets and overall dishonesty with self and others, there may be much more than I know, but this would be difficult to prove. What I do know for certain is that there were many dysfunctional patterns. In my birth family, my parents got pregnant on the first date. My birth father sexually abused me, and my birth mother was prone to both depression and fits of anger when overwhelmed. She says that she only felt bonded to me when nursing, and she was told to stop this when I was three months old. She would leave the family at times to pursue sexual and romantic intrigue with other men. Her birth father died young in a motorcycle accident, and her stepfather's family had alcohol abuse in several members.

Both families harbored secrets, communicated poorly about emotions, and struggled with cohesion versus independence. In the case of my birth family, my mother's side had some family cohesion but also a strong sense of individuality that could lead to disengagement. My birth father's side was even less connected, as evidenced by the fact that as adults, my father and his siblings barely talk. This is not out of animosity; they simply don't think about it much. When my birth mother would disappear at times early in their marriage, my birth father missed her but also enjoyed the solitude. Where many people might panic or feel other strong emotions, he figured that after a few days of her being gone, he should contact some of her friends to see if they knew where she went. It is hard to image such a laissez-faire attitude from someone who grew up in anything but a dysfunctional family.

This lack of deep communication also likely helped create an atmosphere in which abuse was hidden and thus more possible. Sexual abuse happened to both my birth father and birth mother, and my birth father in turn did it to me. My birth mother did not do anything like this, but when she flew into anger, she sometimes threatened my safety. In her depression, she became convinced that she was the worst mother on earth. Each carried their own guilt and likely shame around their behavior, much of which was not openly discussed.

Thus, they decided to put me up for adoption and they didn't tell their families they were doing so, in part to keep anyone in either family from adopting me. True to the dysfunctional family patterns in which they had been raised, there was no communication within the family, choices were removed through deceit, and decisions were made based on fear, guilt, and desperation. In a more functional family dynamic, they might have been able to talk about their struggles and get support. Instead, they carried out the adoption to the surprise and dismay of relatives on both sides. They were disowned by both families for some time as a result.

Like their extended family relationships, their marriage did not survive the adoption either. Again, in a more functional dynamic, they might have pulled through. Lest the reader think they only got married to support my birth mother's pregnancy, they both say they found each other very attractive. This is proven by the fact that they married each other again a few years later, when I was long gone. Shortly after, they divorced again. It is not that they didn't love each other, it's more likely that the weight of intergenerational dysfunctionality was simply too much for them to overcome.

In my new adoptive family, dysfunctional patterns abounded as well. Power was concentrated in the hands of my father, who struggled with addiction to alcohol for almost his entire adult life. This could not be openly stated in our family and thus could not be addressed. Excuses and lies were offered instead, often that "daddy was tired." At times, he woke us up with drunken ranting, demanding that we answer nonsensical questions. The next morning, we were expected to act as if this had not happened, and in fact tiptoe around dad, coddling the family member who had caused all the trouble.

Through this, I learned to be deceptive and manipulative, for these seemed like my best bet to get through these episodes. Looking back, I could have made other choices, but lived more by reaction than thoughtful response, another casualty to the unhealthy dynamics of both families.

Emotions were not openly discussed, save anger, which only my father could express without repercussions. My father had open disdain for "people who share every bowel movement with each other." This was said in response to my journey in therapy and other healing modalities. I remember well the handful of times that I heard or saw my mom express her fear or sadness over my dad's alcohol use, only to be met with a torrent of anger and threats, sometimes being called foul names that I never otherwise heard.

I may have been raised in difficult circumstances, but my father had been raised with worse. His mother displayed signs of narcissism, which does not lend itself to functional family dynamics. She terrorized our home emotionally whenever she came to stay with us. She was demanding of my mother, who did never set any boundaries that I saw. This grandmother had in turn been adopted, and told me once of her resultant suffering. She undoubtedly wanted me to know I was not alone.

I say this to point out that in this story of all these dysfunctional patterns, there was no one person to blame. Everyone I have spoken of loved me and others in their family. They were all, in my estimation, doing the best they could with what they had and how they had been raised.

How far back do the family patterns go? How often in one generation or another has addiction reared its ugly head and pushed the family dynamic in an unhealthy direction? Did anyone before my generation know they could safely ask for help? There is no way to answer these questions. Thus, compassion for myself and everyone else in the family makes much more sense than blame. As a happy result, I have more peace in my heart.

This compassion doesn't mean I passively accept all the dysfunctional family patterns. I have done my best to challenge them wherever I can. I speak openly about how I am really doing when asked, including if the question comes from family members who seem to prefer surface-level small talk. I don't insist that they open up to me, but I try to model what I want in these relationships. I ask if they are open to feedback, and do my best to offer it by sharing my own experience, strength, and hope, rather than trying to tell them how they should change. I have worked hard to stop active addiction in my family and embrace active recovery instead.

If my story reminds you in some ways of your story or that of your extended family, you may fear that the challenges are too great. I am here to tell you this is not so. The patterns in your family may run deep, but this only means that more effort may be required, never that it is impossible.

As more and more recovery options become available and better known, family members may start to look for better ideas than those that were passed down to them. Perhaps someone in the family goes to treatment or finds lasting change through a recovery fellowship. One of them may start to read a great recovery book or attend weekly therapy, finding healthier patterns to insert into the family dynamic. The old habits may pop back up when that person is under sufficient stress, but they more and more quickly return to their newer healthy patterns. Other family members may be inspired by these new choices and their more favorable outcomes. With sufficient time and effort, recovery becomes part of the family pattern and dynamic, and is now part of what gets passed down from generation to generation.

By the nature of family dynamics, in which a change in one family member affects all the others, making positive change will shake things up. Some family members may become threatened and, consciously or not, may challenge the one who is changing. The person newly in recovery may find other family members nudging them back toward their old patterns. This could be as blatant as encouraging the recovering person to use alcohol again ("You've been doing so well that you can probably have just one with us") or more subtle, such as mourning the loss of addictive personality traits ("I miss how much fun you were at parties"). Perhaps most subtle of all is when the family simply assumes that the person in recovery has not really changed and treats them accordingly. This is very understandable, especially if trust has been broken many times, or the addicted family member has had multiple attempts at sobriety that always seem to end the same way. In such cases, the person who is newly in recovery may have a long road ahead in which they will have to resist the invitations to return to their old dysfunctional patterns.

This can also happen when you get into recovery as a family member. The person with addiction may be upset that you are no longer playing out the old patterns or falling for the old tricks. Other family members may also give you a hard time for not rescuing the person with the addiction. They may still be convinced that the person with addiction can be talked out of it, or that giving them money "one more time" will finally do the trick. They may push you hard to step back into your old role, believing in their hearts that this is the best thing for everyone.

The good news is that if you or anyone else sticks to recovery, the rest of the family will eventually adjust to the new normal. This may in turn inspire other family members to try new ways of being for themselves. As mentioned earlier in this book, this can lead to multiple family members getting into recovery over time. Thus, the family dynamics as a whole can start to shift from less functional to more functional. This is not easy to do, but I can think of few endeavors more worthy or fulfilling.

In my own family, I have been able to contribute to this shift. When I went out looking for a life partner, I had one major criterion in mind: I needed to be with someone who was willing to work on themselves and on the relationship. This led to starting our marriage out with six years of weekly individual and couples therapy with a great therapist. I was scared going into this process but I knew I didn't want to back down on that commitment to change. When the time came to enter recovery, ten years into our marriage, I knew that our commitment to change was being put to the test again, but it was a test we had passed many times. When my wife entered recovery, I was able to support her as best I could, just as she had done for me. Throughout over three decades of marriage, we have known that whatever life threw at us, we could communicate as openly as we knew how, change both individually and together, and be there for each other throughout the process. There were times I thought we would not make it, but whenever we were faced with the choice, we were able to make our lives together more functional.

When our daughter was born, we knew we wanted to raise her in a more functional dynamic. We did not succeed in every moment, yet we were clear in both thought and action that our family was committed to being flexible, growing together, communicating honestly and openly, and to recovering from both childhood trauma and the effects of intergenerational patterns of addiction on both sides. Our daughter has thanked us more than once for bringing the culture of recovery into our home and raising her with this foundation. I feel great knowing we are contributing to intergenerational healing, helping family members down the line who I may never meet but whose lives will be better because we put the effort in now.

Family Roles

In every family, each person plays a role. While almost anyone would agree with that statement, these roles do not easily fall into neat categories that are scientifically measurable[1], yet the idea of family roles still gives people a framework with which to conceptualize what is happening in their family. It should be noted that almost all research that supports these ideas, including the effects of birth order, is based in educated, industrialized Western countries. Findings are mixed and the evidence weaker for other cultures.[2]

With that in mind, we will look at some of the most common roles that people take. Each role has strengths and limitations, and each can have a distinct effect on addiction and recovery.

There is no one set of clearly defined roles, but many American theorists go with some version the following[1]:

1. Family Hero
2. Lost Child
3. Enabler
4. Mascot
5. Scapegoat

In this framework, people can take on more than one role, but will tend to have one as their "home base." This is the role to which they will habitually return, especially in times of stress or crisis. They may change roles when they move out of the house but then find themselves going back to their old role when they go home for family gatherings. Sometimes this can even be a source of frustration for them and a surprise for their partners who know them primarily in other settings.

Let's look at each role and see its pros and cons, especially in light of addiction.

Family Hero

The Family Hero is the golden child of the family. Stereotypically, this will be the oldest child, who is the only one of the siblings who has some period of time as the only child. They will thus have had the experience of being most in tune with the parents and will be more likely to want to please them. They will also be the only ones to dodge the experience of having other kids ahead of them to take up roles already. Instead, they can bask in the glory of each achievement without competition. When other kids come on the scene, the Family Hero may work harder to cement their favored place in the parents' eyes. They may see themselves as the natural leader of the other kids. Family Heroes will be expected to excel, often in more than one area. They may make this look effortless as they display traits such as being organized, decisive, self-disciplined, and goal-oriented.

Every role serves an important purpose in the family. The Family Hero makes the family look good while reassuring the parents that they are doing a good job. This boosts morale because it feels like a win for everyone.

As they grow up, the Family Hero will likely recreate their role in other settings. This might include school, social groups, and the working world. Look for the Family Hero to move up into management and administration. They will be more likely to thrive within whatever system is presented to them.

If that system is a family in which one or both parents are addicted, the Family Hero will likely take on a parenting role to younger siblings and even the parents if they are both in the throes of their disease. This will be the child who helps a hungover parent get up on time, makes excuses for them if necessary, fixes meals, and does anything else that needs doing. Such a child may grow up to be high-functioning in society but never learn to relax. They may also seek partners who need rescuing, feeling most secure when in the role of caregiver and savior.

If it is the Family Hero who becomes addicted, they may use their high achievements to mask their problems. They may also have difficulty asking for help, for fear of tarnishing their image and disappointing others. They are used to conquering any task set before them, so being unable to beat addiction on their own may be a difficult concept for them to accept. They may also be in a primary role in their family systems and tell themselves they can't take time for treatment or meetings because they are so vital for everyone else's wellbeing. In some cases, they will see their addictive acting out as justified because they work so hard. They may also count on certain drugs to help them perform in their heroic role. On the positive side, if the Family Hero is addicted, fear of ruining their image may become an incentive to get help before they lose it all.

If the Family Hero gets into recovery, they must be cautious to not get back up on the pedestal if they are doing well. Others may encourage their progress by saying, "You've got this," or words to that effect, but such sentiments can lead to the overconfidence that precedes a relapse. Instead, the Family Hero would do best to practice humility so that they can tell others honestly when they are struggling. During early recovery, they may have to resist internal and external pressure to return to their high-achieving role right away. Instead, they should give themselves time and space to recover before taking anything else on.

The Family Hero in recovery can use their strengths to propel them to getting written assignments done, making it to all the meetings, and doing service work. They may struggle with not being the one others turn to when they need help, but even this can motivate them to work hard on their recovery so they can become an AA sponsor or SMART facilitator when the time comes.

Lost Child

The Lost Child, sometimes called the Hidden or Silent Child, is stereotypically a middle child. If they have a Family Hero for an older sibling, they may grow up in the shadow of that golden child. While parents do not intend for this to happen, it is natural that there is less time and energy to devote to each child when there are more than one, especially if they are close in age. Additionally, there is typically less novelty in each milestone for the second child. Many a family photo collection has more pictures of the first child's infant and toddler years than the second child's equivalent moments. Finally, some theorists would say that later children seek to carve out their own place in the family system. Thus, if the role of Family Hero is already taken, the next child may chart their own course by enhancing other traits.

These traits typically show up in the Lost Child as introversion, self-sufficiency, and solitary creativity. In group activities, the Lost Child will tend toward a supporting place. They often will appear to be easy-going and willing to follow others' lead, although this may mask an underlying anxiety or fear of conflict. They may also be most comfortable avoiding the spotlight, which means they often fly right down the middle in opinions and achievements. For instance, the Lost Child may tend toward average grades or work performance, because doing too well or too badly will lead to getting more attention than they want. They may hide their feelings and opinions, either because they don't expect anyone to care or because it might generate attention and conflict.

The Lost Child helps the family by being easy to manage and avoiding family tension. This keeps the parents from feeling overwhelmed while making them look good by behaving well and being "no trouble at all."

The Lost Child will tend to recreate their role outside of the home as they move into the larger world of school and then work and adult social life. The Lost Child may make a great roommate because they will be quiet and keep to themselves. They will also make good co-workers who are not striving to compete too much. Some will be drawn to the arts, particularly solitary creative pursuits such as writing or painting.

If one or both parents are addicted, the Lost Child may adapt by exaggerating the qualities of staying quiet and out of the way, perhaps retreating to their room and staying there rather than dealing with the addicted parents. They will probably avoid conflict at all costs, and so are unlikely to challenge the addiction, instead taking on an attitude of,

"What can I do anyway?" This attitude, which seems cynical or even accepting on the surface, may hide anxiety and frustration.

If the Lost Child becomes addicted, they may use their traits of flying under the radar and appearing easy-going to keep the problem hidden. Since the Lost Child is often quiet, solitary, and self-sufficient, family members may miss otherwise obvious signs of addiction. If these suspicions do arise, family members may doubt themselves because they don't want to challenge the person who has always denied needing anything. The Lost Child may count on certain drugs to help them escape into their private worlds, or even to help them get in touch with their creativity if they are the artistic type.

When the Lost Child gets into recovery, dangers include their tendency to blend in without asking for what they need, and being less likely to request help and support even though people in recovery often struggle without it. They may avoid the spotlight to the point that they don't volunteer to help lead a meeting or get contact information of other group members, two things that research shows can help predict success in recovery.[3]

The Lost Child in recovery can also draw on the strengths of their role. This can include leveraging the trait of self-sufficiency by quietly getting their recovery assignments done, helping to keep the meeting running behind the scenes, and not needing a lot of prompting to stay on course. They don't seek praise for their recovery, although they are likely to be grateful for it even if they deny this.

The Enabler

The Enabler, sometimes also called the Family Social Worker, is the person in the family who runs around trying to make sure everyone else is okay. They may be the translator between other family members who are in conflict and they may be the person who best understands what every other family member wants. The Enabler tends to be compassionate, a good listener, and is always available to lend a helping hand. They often struggle with the compulsion to fix others, may not easily receive help or ask for what they need, can be overly forgiving of unacceptable behavior, carry guilt and anxiety, and may fear anger and conflict. They often help others at least in part to deflect from their own inner struggles.

The Enabler helps the family by holding everyone together and being there when others are having issues. They are sometimes the beating heart of the family system, without which the family might have trouble getting by. They can help the family avoid conflicts through their talent at facilitating communication.

As the Enabler moves beyond the family system, they will likely find other situations in which they can play the part of the fixer. If they are not careful, they will develop a social circle filled with people who need help and who may not notice when the Enabler's needs are not getting met. Some Enablers will deliberately set up such relationships so that they always have someone to rescue, thus providing themselves a sense of security. This may eventually lead to frustration and resentment that they are always giving more than they get back, although they may be tempted to hide this. The Enabler may seek careers in the helping professions, such as social work, counseling, or nursing.

If one or both of the Enabler's parents are addicted, the Enabler is likely to kick into high gear. They will have great job security as the child who makes sure the parent appears to be functioning normally, such as getting them up for work, making their coffee, etc. If there are younger siblings, the Enabler will likely help raise them. Either way, the Enabler is in danger of becoming "parentified" either by becoming parent to the younger children, by switching roles so that they act as parent while the addicted parent acts as child, or both. This can lead to a sense of importance and assumption of responsibility such that the Enabler may feel threatened if help arrives or if the addicted parent gets sober. Notice how much this overlaps with the Family Hero's reaction to one or both parents being addicted. One child may take on both roles, or there may be competition for who gets to be the "the most valuable helper."

If the Enabler becomes the addicted one, they may mask their problems by helping others and highlighting everyone else's needs over their own. They may even fall for their own hype and think they can't have that bad a problem if they are still there for the people around them. They may also justify their addictive acting out by telling themselves that they deserve the escape since they are working so hard to make sure everyone else is okay.

When the Enabler enters recovery, there is danger that they will focus on others too much. They may find themselves taking on too many service commitments if they see this as their only value to others. They may get overly concerned with others' recovery and lose focus on their own. If the Enabler is not careful, they may do this so much that they lead themselves right out of recovery altogether. An Enabler may already have relationships with needy people who may not like the changes they see in recovery. Such people may object to the Enabler learning to care for themselves rather than always focusing on the partner's needs. This becomes especially dangerous if the Enabler is in relationship with someone else who has an addiction. The partner may nudge the Enabler to relapse, whether they consciously intend this or not, just to get the old dynamic back.

Of course, the Enabler can also draw on the strengths of their family role. They are people who naturally tend to do service, which is a major part of any recovery program. The Enabler also has to have some qualities as a self-starter in order to run around making sure others are okay, and they can use this "get it done" attitude to fuel their own recovery as well.

The Mascot

The Mascot is the cute and funny one, often the class clown and life of the party. This is stereotypically one of the younger children. Traits include a great sense of humor, flexibility, and an ability to relieve tension, stress, and emotional pain through laughter. The downside of this role includes traits such as a need for attention, lack of focus, tendency to distract others, and impulsivity. The Mascot may also be prone to depression and anxiety underneath their humor, and most likely has difficulty expressing these feelings, let alone dealing with them.

The Mascot helps the family by defusing tension in the family system. They also may help to keep everyone together since they are often the person everyone likes even in the midst of family conflict.

As the Mascot moves out into the world, they will try to keep their familiar role by being the life of the party and the person with a joke handy. They will be well-liked in school or work, but typically don't find high achievement in either arena. They may be drawn to careers in entertainment, especially as performers. A small handful of these may become highly successful but will have trouble turning their stage persona off in their personal lives, leaving them prey to unhappiness behind the façade of constant humor or a glamorous image.

In families where one or both parents are addicted, the Mascot becomes a kind of peacemaker, metaphorically or literally dancing as fast as they can to keep everyone distracted from the seemingly unbearable and unsolvable problems that addiction presents. As they grow into adolescence, the humor might take on a more cynical or angry tone. The Mascot may decide this is the only safe way to express frustration and distress at the family situation.

If it is the Mascot who is addicted, the humor stops protecting their deeper feelings and instead starts protecting the addiction. By being the life of the party and always showing good cheer, they avoid difficult conversations about how bad the addiction has become. They can laugh off any challenge to their acting out and give the impression that there is nothing to be concerned about. They may even get to the point that people enjoy them more under the influence, and thus be encouraged to use alcohol or other drugs. Alternatively, they may fear that if they stop using, no one will want them to be around. After all, the Mascot counts on being entertaining to feel okay.

When the Mascot enters recovery, they may have difficulty getting serious and letting others see their struggle. The tendency to always hide behind a façade of good cheer will be tempting but should be resisted. This can feel uncomfortable, but it is an effort well worth undertaking.

Luckily, humor in a healthy balance can be a great asset in recovery, so the Mascot doesn't have to give up all their familiar traits. In fact, their social nature and ability to be well-liked can help them fit into the new group of people in a recovery fellowship, and ease the burdens of early recovery for themselves and others by cracking a well-timed joke, as long as they can also settle down and get real.

The Scapegoat

The Scapegoat is the one to regularly draw negative attention to themselves. This is stereotypically one of the younger children. Common traits include honesty and expression of emotions (although typically in negative ways), leadership (although in negative directions), and creativity. The Scapegoat struggles with authority and responsibility, has difficulty trusting others, has anger issues, and engages in self-destructive behavior.

This role is helpful to the family by drawing attention away from other family issues and concentrating it on "the one with the problem." Remember the idea of the Identified Patient? The Scapegoat does a great job of fitting into that role, frustrating the other family members but also giving them an excuse to avoid looking at their own issues.

The idea of a scapegoat is a very old one, seen in Hebrew texts from thousands of years ago. These writings describe a ritual in which all the sins of the people were put on a goat and then the goat was sent off into the wilderness, taking the sins of the people with it.[4] In the family system, the Scapegoat similarly takes on the "sins of the family" and is metaphorically exiled through their disapproval. Thus, the person who gets the most complaints is in fact helping everyone else by providing a convenient reason to downplay or ignore their own problems.

The Scapegoat will often have issues outside of the home as well, although they may be liked by people who see through the role and focus instead on the hurting person underneath. The Scapegoat may attempt to push supportive people away while secretly basking in the positive attention, or they may openly embrace these relationships and flourish. To the family's frustration, the Scapegoat may go back to more destructive and self-sabotaging behaviors at home or away from the supportive people. They may also take on leadership qualities outside of the home even if they are leading others in negative directions. Especially in adolescence, the Scapegoat often gravitates towards other Scapegoats, often entrenching them further into this role as it becomes a badge of pride and belonging.

If the Scapegoat has one or more addicted people as parents, they become vital to the family system by distracting everyone inside and out of the family from the parent's issues. Even if an insightful teacher, social worker, or other helpful adult sees through this, the family will often deny or downplay the parent's problems and prefer to focus on the Scapegoat child. Unsurprisingly, the Scapegoat may come to take on the addictive pattern themselves as they grow older.

I know I certainly did. As the family Scapegoat, I was the focal point of much heartache and many parent-teacher conferences. Some teachers saw me as a frustrating case who needed a military academy or stronger discipline, others as a special kid who was just misunderstood and needed the right kind of encouragement to thrive. Both had a point, but to the best of my knowledge, no one stopped to ask if anything was going on in the home. The focus was on me and how to get me to live up to my potential, or at least behave in a reasonable manner, not whether one or both of my parents might be struggling. I was oblivious to all this and went about doing whatever I thought I could get away with to help me escape my reality. This made me the center of attention, pulling focus away from my dad's alcohol use.

After all, he was a highly successful executive in a highly successful company, while I was a child who barely passed each grade level in school, did little to no work, and preferred to live in an internal fantasyland.

In my teen years, both my dad and I became worse. His drinking and anger increased as his highly successful company started to collapse in scandal, while I became sneakier and my addictive acting out got worse. I made an effort to pull my grades up, but also rebelled more, once again providing the family with a focal point to avoid confronting my dad's drinking, anger, and verbal abuse, and my mom's increasing dissatisfaction in the marriage. It never crossed my mind that I might be reacting to what was going on at home, let alone to consciously ask for any help. I found that telling a few friends about my dad's drinking elicited sympathy, but when I told an adult neighbor, he brought it up to my mom and she later lectured me about the dangers of telling anyone outside of our home about dad's problems. In other words, my issues were fair game but my dad's issues were not to be addressed.

Through all this, I swore I would never use alcohol like my father did, and in fact abstained as a teenager while my friends explored mind-altering chemicals. Instead, I went further and further into my sex and love addiction, which eventually led to alcohol use after all. It never crossed my mind that I was repeating family patterns. I felt smugly superior to my dad even though I had only picked a different means of escape. I repeated some of his volatility, exploding unpredictably in anger and then justifying my behavior after the fact. Despite resenting how the family protected my dad's issues through silence, I was hesitant to let anyone know if I was struggling, and in my marriage I still tended to keep our issues private even when talking to supportive people.

Some of this came from my desire to get out of the Scapegoat role. The Family Hero looked a lot more appealing, and I hoped that I could fake it well enough that someday it would come true. I was always afraid that the Scapegoat was my destiny, however, which made it difficult to relax, enjoy my achievements, or accept praise. I found it hard to believe that I could consistently do well without screwing it all up again, and my addiction reinforced this. Though I could self-justify with the best of them, I always shamed myself underneath. Of course, this shame and self-blame only drove me to seek further escape, creating a feedback loop that helped sustain the addiction.

In early recovery, I found that I still carried all that fear. I knew I could work hard at recovery but was afraid that things would all fall apart anyway and that it would inevitably be my fault. My Scapegoat habits were not quiet during this time. I rebelled against the parts of my recovery program that I didn't like, and I was slow to ask for individual help or mentorship from others in the fellowship. This kept me from receiving the deeper help that comes from close connections with others in recovery. Thus, my recovery progressed more slowly than it might have if I had gravitated to another role growing up. Even as an adult with a spouse and child, I took up some of my old Scapegoat attitudes, seeing myself as the Identified Patient of the family. I naturally blamed myself for any issues we had.

To this day, if my wife is struggling, I wonder if it's because of me. Attending a family recovery fellowship helps immensely with this, but that thought still comes up first. The fellowship gives me tools to consider other possibilities and detach with love, thus helping me step away from my old family role whenever it does not serve me or those around me.

Here are some things that made it easier. I attended weekly individual therapy sessions for the first few years of my recovery. I started to grow more comfortable in my own skin. I found that some of the Scapegoat traits could serve me in positive ways. For instance, when my recovery fellowship seemed to be getting embroiled in outside political issues, I had no problem speaking up and eventually splitting off to start of new meeting that would stay out of such matters. In this way, my old habit of doing my own thing regardless of what others thought, and to some extent my ability to lead against the establishment, helped to create a new meeting in town and protect my recovery.

Through my story, you can see that when the Scapegoat becomes addicted, this can seem like a natural extension of their family role. They remain the focus of the family and may take on negative traits of their addicted parent but differentiate by using a different drug or an entirely different addiction. If the Scapegoat finds recovery, they may struggle with taking direction or fully joining in a group. These traits can serve the Scapegoat though, such as by making it easier to speak uncomfortable truths when no one else will, and to do what is best for their recovery regardless of what anyone else thinks.

Having looked at each family role, I encourage you to see how you can use this model to benefit you and your understanding of your family. Recognize how some of these roles may show up in your family of origin and in your current family if you have created a new one. Everyone may not fit neatly or perfectly into this model, but you may find generalities that help you understand your family dynamics. Look for opportunities for role flexibility. For instance, if you or one of your family members tends to be the Family Hero, it can be helpful to not only thank them for the strengths they bring to the family, but also encourage them to explore some of the characteristics of another family role, such as taking time for themselves and pursuing personal interests like the

Lost Child. Having a conversation about family roles, especially with affected children, can give everyone a chance to look at what strengths they exhibit in their most comfortable role, and what strengths they want to try from another family role. Be sure to model this by being flexible in your own role. This allows greater balance in the family dynamic and gives you freedom to express different parts of yourself.

I was given a powerful example of role flexibility when a friend's mother was hospitalized due to complications from years of alcohol abuse enabled by a dysfunctional family dynamic. When his mother was hallucinating due to detox in the hospital, it seemed clear to everyone in the family that it was time for her to get help. However, as soon as she started to feel better, the family started downplaying how bad things had gotten and got ready to go back to business as usual, backing away from any suggestion of treatment. My friend, who usually played the Lost Child, suddenly realized he needed to draw from strengths more commonly seen in the Scapegoat. He did this by speaking up, saying the things that everyone knew but were getting ready to sweep under the rug: that mom was not doing well and needed help. The rest of the family seemed surprised at this, but once it had been said out loud, action was taken, mom got treatment, and she was able to establish sustained sobriety as a result.

We thus see that an understanding of family dynamics and roles, and the willingness to be flexible in each, can allow positive changes to take place within a family. Take some time to see how the things in this chapter may be helpful in not only understanding what is happening, but also in creating change for you and your family as you travel the road of realistic hope.

Chapter 9

Creating Happiness

Greater happiness is possible for your family. If you didn't believe this, there would be little point in reading this book, let alone doing anything I suggest in it. That being said, it can be hard to keep this in mind when addiction is having its way with a loved one. It's important to remember that you can't force happiness on anyone else, but by increasing your own happiness, you will be setting a good example and raising the overall atmosphere in your family. That's why it is so important to have some understanding about how happiness can be created despite the challenges you face. To achieve this, we will be turning to the ideas and techniques of positive psychology to see how they can help you.

Before I go any further, I want to take a moment to give a shout out to my mentor in this, Dr. Jason Powers. He is a pioneer in taking the precepts of positive psychology and applying them specifically to addiction recovery through his Positive Recovery program.[1] I highly encourage you to check out his work. Many of my thoughts here are based on things he taught me, which I then explored further in my own studies. Part of my mission is to teach these ideas to family members so that they can also benefit from this groundbreaking work.

While a full exploration of positive psychology would take another book or two, I want to cover some of the major ideas and look at how they can help you in your journey. This will include getting a better understanding of what research tells us about happiness, a brief overview of positive psychology, and a few ideas that you can put into practice today.

What We Know So Far

People have probably philosophized about happiness for as long as people have philosophized about anything. There have been many theories and earlier scientific efforts to study happiness[2], but until the turn of the 21st century, there hasn't been such a concerted effort to study happiness using scientific principles.[3] That is partly because there has been a common misconception that if unhappiness is removed, then happiness will automatically result, stemming from the medical idea that removing sickness will result in health. Unfortunately, this is not true. Instead, removing unhappiness and doing nothing else can get you to a kind of baseline, which may feel like relief but will not bring more joy and wellbeing into your life. For that, you must work on adding happiness. This turns out to be more about working on your thinking than changing your outside circumstances.

A simple analogy is that if I want to improve my physical fitness, I'll want to cut out junk food. This is a good start, but it doesn't do anything to build muscle. Similarly, getting rid of negative thinking is a great move, but it doesn't automatically get me thinking positively. Instead, positive thinking is a skill that can and should be exercised regularly. As with all such skills, this will come more easily to some than to others, but everyone can improve with practice.

Another important finding is that unhappiness doesn't have to be all cleared out before work on happiness can begin[4]. It turns out that people can improve their happiness level no matter what their circumstances. To paraphrase an Al-Anon saying, no situation is so bad that it can't improve, and nobody is so unhappy that they can't become happier. This is not achieved by changing all the outside circumstances in your life so that they match what you think will make you happy. Outside change can feel wonderful, but the positive effects tend to be temporary. Instead, deep and fulfilling happiness comes from changing inside circumstances, which is all about changing how you think about yourself and your life.

In my own life, I struggled because I thought that I had to get my family members to behave a certain way in order for me to be happy. Whether it was my childhood schemes to get my dad to stop drinking alcohol, adult efforts to convince my wife to dress and act the way I thought she should, or parenting strategies to get my daughter to do her homework, it was all about my certainty that if they would change their behavior, I would feel okay. I rarely thought of it so explicitly, but if I am honest with myself, that was my goal.

Along with getting people to behave, I also believed I needed to be a professional musician, preferably a rock star, in order to be fulfilled. I thought everyone needed to see me as I wished to be seen, and that if I had more money, sex, shiny new things, etc., then I would have happiness. When my life didn't go the way I wanted, I grew sad, fearful, and angry. I felt that the outside circumstances were keeping me from feeling happy. To make things worse, sometimes everything went exactly as I wanted, but the happiness was always fleeting. As a result, I tried even harder to get everything to line up again, or I lived in fear of losing the things I thought were making me happy.

When I turned to my inside circumstances, I got better results but could still fall for some of the same thinking traps. I told myself that once I got rid of every unhappiness, I would finally feel okay. Needless to say, this did not go much better. I have had the benefit of working with a couple of brilliant therapists in my time, and they helped immensely, but healing the traumas and negative thinking in my life did not automatically create joy.

That took its own work. Looking back, I didn't need to wait for all the issues to be resolved before I could start building a solid foundation of happiness and fulfillment in my life. I could have started that on day one if I had been more open to it. I'm glad I didn't have to wait for all the yucky stuff to be gone, because issues and negative thinking still come up. The difference today is that I not only have more tools and experience to deal with those issues, but I also practice positive thinking skills every day.

Research shows that this kind of regular practice of positive psychology techniques can improve happiness in people who deal with adverse outside circumstances, but also in people who have difficult inside circumstances, such as mental health issues.[4] This is important to know for those who are struggling with addiction in themselves or a loved one. Addiction and other mental health issues often go hand in hand. No matter which one came first, it is likely to exacerbate the other. Knowing that happiness doesn't have to wait until all these things are resolved can be a relief for those who see a lifelong battle ahead of themselves.

Concepts of Positive Psychology

Core concepts of positive psychology include PERMA, a focus on strengths, resilience, and the power of gratitude. Positive psychology does not downplay the importance of recognizing and dealing with what goes wrong. Instead, it shows that it is possible and even necessary to build happiness at the same time. We will take a broad overview of these ideas.

PERMA

PERMA is an acronym, referring to five aspects of human happiness: Positive Emotions, Engagement, Relationships, Meaning, and Achievement.[5] According to the principles of positive psychology, each is important and should be sought in balance with the others. PERMA can now be measured by a scientific survey,[5] correlates well with other ways to measure wellbeing,[6] shows relevance, if not always perfectly, across different cultures,[7, 8] and interfaces with other positive psychology concepts like character strengths.[9]

Here's a brief explanation of each aspect:

Positive Emotions – This refers to the idea that we all need to have emotionally positive experiences in our lives. This might include a moment with a friend, feeling sunshine on our face, smelling a rose, enjoying delicious food, receiving affirmation, doing something thrilling, listening to music, or any other experience that feels intrinsically pleasurable. Such experiences contribute to a "pleasant life." While this is vital, it should not be mistaken for the whole enchilada.

Addicted people may seem to be seeking a constant external stream of pleasurable experiences, most likely in an attempt to deal with a constant internal stream of negative thoughts and feelings. What is mistaken for pleasure in these cases is thus really relief from discomfort. In its attempts to stay in balance, the addicted brain dampens its ability to feel natural pleasure, leaving this aspect of happiness elusive during active addiction and for a time in early recovery. If recovery is sustained, the response to such naturally pleasant experiences will return, although this will often take months. In your own recovery, it will be important to find pleasant experiences for yourself both as an act of self-care and to take the focus off trying to control your addicted loved one.

Engagement – We all need experiences that captivate and inspire us. Such experiences usually include a sense of "flow," in which we no longer focus on the time involved, but instead find ourselves immersed in what we are doing for its own sake. These experiences often challenge us to grow in some way, such as becoming more adept at a skill or acquiring new knowledge in an area of interest. Examples include playing music, athletics, education in something that fascinates you, training dogs, playing video games, playing chess, gardening, or any other activity that includes a sense of interest and challenge. As you move your focus from your loved one's recovery to your own, seek that sense of engagement by discovering a new interest or rekindling one that may have gone neglected.

Relationships – Human beings are not human beings unless they have relationships. As children, we define ourselves by our connections to our parents, siblings, extended family, friends, neighbors, teachers, and classmates. As adolescents, we seek out peer groups with a new urgency, thinking of ourselves as belonging to these groups in a way that feels more important than it may at any other time in our lives. We also take a new interest in potential relationships to romantic and eventually sexual partners. As we transition into adulthood, we may define ourselves by changing relationships with parents and the family in which we were raised. If we start families of our own, we invert the relationships with which we started as we take the role of the parent, with new people (literally) in the role of our children.

When these relationships feel positive, they contribute greatly to our happiness. When the relationships go badly, we tend to suffer as a result. This is especially true when it is our primary relationships that are in trouble, as often happens around addiction. Thus, we feel a strong instinctive drive to heal those relationships and bring happiness back. In my experience, loss of relationship is one of the most powerful fears that plagues people around addiction. This is the likely root of the codependent and enabling behaviors discussed in earlier sections of this book, because family members fear losing relationship with their addicted loved ones so much that they will resort to unreasonable behaviors in an attempt to get the relationship back.

For some family members, this means they will have to shore up or create new relationships if their addicted loved ones have not found recovery. This will work better than trying desperately to wrest this vital aspect of happiness from people who are not in a position to provide it. I am not saying you need to abandon your addicted loved ones, only that you should expand your circle so that you are not leaning on addicted people for as much of your relationship needs. This highlights one of the many benefits of connecting with a recovery fellowship: it gives you a ready source of healthier relationships with supportive people.

Meaning – This is considered by some to be the most important aspect of happiness. Friedrich Nietzsche famously said, "He who has a why to live for can bear almost any how."[10] In other words, if we experience meaning in our lives and purpose in our actions, we can get through circumstances that are unpleasant or even threaten to be overwhelming. Research confirms that seeking meaning can help with the deepest grief[11] or finding growth in circumstances more often associated with psychological harm.[12] This may be helpful to those who struggle with the fear, or worse the reality, of losing a loved one to addiction.

Meaning may be found through spirituality, close relationships, creating art, experiences of awe and wonder, and anything that feels like it contributes to the greater good. The most powerful experiences of meaning are those in which someone feels that they are being of service in some way, especially if they are contributing to something good that is larger than themselves. This may involve things like helping or teaching a child, volunteering to walk dogs at a local rescue shelter, feeding the homeless, painting an uplifting public mural, or helping others to find emotional healing.

As a family member, you may find yourself constantly trying to help your addicted loved one even if they don't seem to want it or rarely respond in the ways you hoped. Consider that the world has so many other opportunities to be of service. You might find greater meaning in life by reaching out to someone who really wants the help.

Achievement – These are the milestones along the road of happiness. Achievements can be daily things like making your bed or getting all your work done before heading home, the culmination of practice like learning to play a new piece on the piano or marking a new personal best in athletics, or longer-term goals such as writing a book or getting a career award.

Achievements can be highly valued and are necessary to show progress and the rewards of effort, but like Positive

Emotions, can be mistakenly thought of as all a person needs. This belief can leave people chasing the next achievement and then the next, thinking each one will bring lasting happiness. This usually ends in disappointment and feeling like nothing is ever enough. Sometimes people in early recovery get caught in this trap because they fear they have wasted so much time spent in addiction or focused on others. They often want to rush into a flurry of activity to make up for this. If you or your loved one seem to be falling into this way of thinking, strive instead to bring this part of your life into balance. Enjoy the achievements large and small as an opportunity to reflect on progress in your life and recovery, rather than seeing them as the end goal.

The ideas of PERMA can be seen throughout the culture of recovery fellowships, which foster positive emotions, encourage members to engage through things like sharing in meetings and the written exercises of each program, build relationships with people at the meetings, offer meaning through volunteering to help others recover, and celebrate achievements such as reaching a new phase in SMART, completion of one of the Twelve Steps in Al-Anon, or just counting the success of another day spent in recovery.

Want to improve how PERMA is showing up in your life? Take a few moments to look over each aspect of happiness, then rate each one between 0-20. Next, add all the scores together. This gives you a baseline score between 0-100 of how you are currently experiencing overall happiness in your life. Now look over the aspects in contrast with each other. Which ones are doing best? Which ones could benefit from improvement? Brainstorm some ideas about how to bolster the areas in which you scored lowest. Talk with a trusted friend or advisor about your ideas and get some feedback (this builds Relationship) and then make a list of ideas you have gotten. Spend some time contemplating what it will be like to add some of this happiness to your life (Positive Emotions) and then set about accomplishing some of the things on your list (Achievement). If some of the things on your list promote Engagement and Meaning, then all the better. After you have done some of the things on your list, rate the aspects of PERMA again to see how your overall score and each aspect are doing. This gives you a way to find what is working best for you and note the progress in your journey of building happiness in your life.

A Focus on Strengths

Another one of the foundational ideas in positive psychology is that all people have innate strengths and that focusing on these is just as important as offering healing for pathology.[13] In order to move this into an actionable idea, some of the pioneers of positive psychology set about to compile a book of identifiable character strengths to counter the more well-known books of diagnosable mental disorders. To do this, they looked through the literature of major world cultures throughout different time periods to find common themes in the virtues (big ideas of moral excellence) and values (how these ideas show up in someone's life) that seem most universal. This led to the distillation of six virtues, which in turn were broken down into a total of 24 values.[13]

Here is a list of the virtues, with the associated strengths listed below each virtue.

Wisdom and Knowledge
- Creativity
- Curiosity
- Judgment
- Love of learning
- Perspective

Courage
- Bravery
- Perseverance
- Honesty
- Zest

Humanity
- Love
- Kindness
- Social intelligence

Justice

- Teamwork
- Fairness
- Leadership

Temperance

- Forgiveness
- Humility
- Prudence
- Self-regulation

Transcendence

- Appreciation of beauty and excellence
- Gratitude
- Hope
- Humor
- Spirituality

Positive psychologists worked to come up with reliable and verifiable ways to measure these values so that they have some validity in a scientific sense, much in the way that there are ways to verify a given pathological diagnosis. This led to the creation of the VIA Survey. As of this writing, it can be taken by anyone freely at any time at viacharacter.org, which is sponsored by the University of Pennsylvania. The survey will give a ranking of how the 24 strengths show up in your life.

The results are not considered immutable, but instead are a good way to see what strengths are dominant right now.

The strengths are like muscles: they can be exercised and improved through deliberate effort. Some will come more naturally, and these are referred to as your signature strengths. They are likely to be the top five or six on your VIA results. None, however, are out of reach. If there is a character strength you admire in others, that is because it is in you somewhere, perhaps looking for expression.

I tell you all this in a book about addiction for two main reasons. First, many people who love someone with addiction need to rediscover their strengths because their self-esteem can take a hit as a result of that relationship. Sometimes, the person with the addiction tears down those around them as a way to deflect from their otherwise obvious problem or perhaps as a way to cope with their own shame. Other times, it is simply the result of loved ones feeling helpless to save the addicted person. Either way, a reminder of core strengths is in order. Those who grew up around addiction may not be rebuilding their self-esteem so much as discovering it for the first time. Positive psychology in general, and the VIA classification of strengths in particular, can be a good way to start this process.

The second reason I bring up the strengths-based approach is because when people are in the throes of active addiction, they often show up at their worst. By the time they enter recovery, everyone in the family may have lost sight of each other's strengths. At the very least, those strengths have often been obscured, and family members can become alarmed or angry at the slightest hint that the old behaviors and attitudes are back. Some family members are not in any mood to affirm or even support the person who is newly in recovery, because the hurt is too fresh or too deep. Seeing this, the person with addiction may become defensive and tempted to fire back or give up. If everyone can learn to view each other through a strengths-based lens, such flare-ups can be diminished or even eliminated.

One way to do this is through strength-spotting. Just like it sounds, this is all about deliberately looking for the strengths displayed in yourself and the people around you. You might start by looking over the VIA list. Pick three strengths that stand out in each of your family members. Take a few moments and think of all the ways that each strength shows up in their lives. Notice what it's like to make this your central focus, and how you feel about each family member after concentrating on their strengths. Consider how it might feel to look at everyone in your life, including yourself, through this lens.

In my own life and recovery, this has been a powerful tool. When my brain is on autopilot, it will tend to pick up on negative traits and features of any situation. Unfortunately, this means that I am more likely to notice what's wrong in myself and the people around me first. This can lead to shame and resentment, two things that do not serve me, my recovery, or my relationships. Taking a strengths-based look at myself and those around me can quickly turn this around. I may have to remind myself to do this, but it makes a big difference in how I see and relate to others and myself.

As an example, I recently started feeling resentful towards my wife (sorry, hon) for areas in our relationship in which she wasn't doing what I wanted her to do. As this resentment built, I noticed I was treating her with less kindness and more criticism. I didn't like my behavior but it was hard to get myself to stop. As I was grappling with this, I remembered to look at her through the lens of her strengths. It's easy to see that she is one of the most loving people I have ever met, which led me to think of all the ways she loves me and has shown that love throughout our time together. I immediately felt the resentment melt away. Nothing in her behavior had to change in order for me to feel better towards her and treat her with more kindness and respect. All it took was concentrating on her strengths.

Resilience

Resilience, or the ability to come back from and even thrive after difficulties, is a key focus in positive psychology. This is also a trait that makes recovery possible. After all, if people weren't resilient, they would not be able to recover from the devastating effects of addiction. This is just as true whether it is their own addiction or someone else's. Extensive research shows a strong correlation between resilience and overall wellbeing, although the relationship is not as straightforward as "resilience leads to wellbeing" or "wellbeing leads to resilience" but is more like "resilience and wellbeing tend to feed each other."[14] Resilience has also been shown to reduce the negative effects of stress, depression, anxiety, and trauma.[15]

The question thus becomes whether resilience is an inborn trait or if it can be learned and developed. The answer seems to be that both are true.[14] Resilience comes more naturally to some than to others. It seems unlikely that there is one resilience gene, but as with all human behavior, a given person's genes will combine with their life experiences to produce personality characteristics and traits such as resilience.

It is worth noting that some resilience patterns may be highly adaptive in one life circumstance and then be detrimental later in the same person's life. Addiction and other dysfunctional behavior can be the result of this shift. If the person in question can find their way to recovery, then the underlying resilience can become a helpful trait again.

For instance, when I was adopted as a toddler, I felt emotionally overwhelmed but needed to keep going and survive. I made an executive decision at 2 ½ years old that my best bet would be to stop fully trusting anyone and go it alone emotionally as much as I could. At the time, this was a much more resilient strategy than curling up in a ball to die. Nonetheless, it caused me problems for a long time afterward. I know this also made things difficult for family and friends who wanted to connect to me and love me. They often scratched their heads at my behavior or just gave up on trying to get too close.

Moving toward adolescence, I began to feel more anger and self-pity at my miserable fate, having long forgotten my survival decision of the past. My life circumstances had completely outgrown my early resilience strategy, but by then I just thought it was who I was. My addictive acting out provided escape and relief, and so it ramped up. By the time the price of this started to become apparent, I had firmly established the neurological pattern that encouraged me to keep going anyway. In other words, my addiction harnessed my resilience, and I continued for about another 20 years.

When I first entered recovery, my natural and developed resilience worked as both a help and a hindrance. It helped when I showed up at meetings believing I could conquer recovery like I had so many other things. It hindered me when I still saw myself as different than others and not subject to their rules. The longer I stayed in recovery, however, the more my resilience helped. I kept showing up to meetings and doing the suggested work even when it was hard. When I relapsed, I got up and got going again immediately. No matter what, I stuck with recovery. Since then, my resilience has been a force for good in my life.

How can resilience be learned and increased? Recent analysis of multiple studies suggests that resilience training, such as group therapy and education, can be beneficial not only during and immediately after the training, but several studies showed that the positive effects were still consistent at six-month follow-ups.[15] The two techniques that showed the best results were Cognitive Behavior Therapy [CBT] and mindfulness training.

CBT is a well-established set of techniques based on the simple premise that if you change the way you think about yourself, your life, and any situation you are in, you will change your feelings and experience. A wide variety of therapeutic techniques are based on CBT, such as EMDR, Dialectical Behavioral Therapy [DBT], etc. CBT has been shown to improve many mental health conditions such as depression and anxiety. SMART Recovery is built around CBT techniques. Despite all this, it is only recently that research has been done to see how CBT positively influences resilience.

One CBT idea that gets used in positive psychology is to work on more positive and realistic thinking about future events. Take a moment now and think about something in your loved one's future. Notice if you tend to catastrophize, which is to say that you expect the worst to happen. For instance, when your loved one is in early recovery you may find that you are on edge waiting to see if relapse is going to happen. Perhaps you feel anxiety about this and so you want to ask them a stream of questions about their recovery and their plans, subconsciously seeking reassurance that they are going to be okay.

Now take a piece of paper and write out that worst-case scenario you have in your head. Next to it, write down how likely this is to happen (0-100%). Next, write down the best-case scenario, and how likely this is to happen (0-100%). Now, see if there is some other outcome that seems more even likely than the best or worst cases, and write this out as well. Note how likely this is to happen (0-100%). Look over all three possibilities, taking a few moments to concentrate on each one. What do you notice in your feelings? Which possibility seemed like the best use of your energy? Make an effort to focus on that one more often. After all, your loved one is not more or less likely to stay sober based on which possibility gets your attention, so you may as well pick the one that helps you most.

To get even more from this exercise, get feedback on what you've written from at least one trustworthy source who knows something about addiction and the family. This might be a member of a recovery fellowship, or it might be a trained professional well-versed in these matters. No matter who it is, listen to hear if they notice things about the situation that you may have missed, or give a perspective that helps you see things in a whole new way. Sometimes just knowing that others understand is helpful.

Based on what you find, revise your original possibilities and percentages, and notice how you feel about the situation now. If you are able to feel better about it, recognize that nothing in the situation itself needed to change in order to improve your feelings. All you had to do is change the way you think about it. If you practice this type of exercise, you will develop greater resilience as you face other scenarios and challenges in your life.

If you want to explore more about CBT, there are any number of books, workbooks, and webpages dedicated to CBT ideas and exercises. Any social worker, therapist, or counselor should be well-versed in CBT. As mentioned earlier, SMART Recovery is based in CBT (sometimes also referred to as REBT).

Next on our list of resilience tools is mindfulness. Mindfulness is the idea of being rooted in the present moment and experience, and accepting that experience as fully as possible. This is in contrast to being preoccupied with the past and future. This can be quite helpful to wellbeing because the present moment is often just fine, whereas guilt, regret, etc. are based in the past, and anxiety and worry are all about the future. Research links mindfulness, particularly the practice of acceptance, with greater resilience in even the most difficult circumstances.[16] Mindfulness has also been shown to help with anxiety, depression, emotional distress, chronic pain, and many other ailments.[17] It meshes well with CBT, leading to some of CBT's more modern iterations, such as DBT.[17]

Mindfulness practices are becoming more and more popular, so it isn't hard to find mindfulness exercises online. Explore these resources and find some techniques that seem like a good starting point for you. Choose one and start working on it until it feels comfortable, then add another and another, and soon you will find yourself living a more mindful life.

One simple idea is to sit still and experience your breathing as fully as you can. You may choose to take long, slow breaths while doing this or you may decide to let the breath flow naturally. Either way, notice everything that goes with each breath. What temperature is the air? How does it feel in your mouth and/or nostrils? How does it feel in your throat? Feel your chest expand and contract. Notice how your diaphragm feels. Follow each breath as it goes through its natural cycle. When your thinking starts to drift, bring it gently back to the breath, making this the center of your attention. Keep this attention for as long as you can. With practice, you will likely be able to go longer and longer, leading to a greater sense of relaxation. You can also focus mindfully on your breath while stuck in traffic, during a stressful meeting at work, or as a way to relax and recenter yourself when you get home in the evening.

Notice how this method of relaxation contrasts with so many of the more common ways people try to relax, such as watching television, playing a game, or reading a novel. Mindfulness leaves you more present in your life. All the others take you away from your life, much as addiction promises to do. As I have asked many of my clients, how much of the rest of your life do you want to spend escaping the rest of your life?

As mindfulness puts you in touch with your present experience, it may also point out opportunities for growth. Many people seem to avoid mindfulness because they fear it will force them to feel their negative feelings or deal with unpleasant truths. While ignoring feelings and facts is an understandable impulse, it makes a terrible long-term strategy because doing so does not make them go away, nor will it lessen their effects on your life.

Instead, consider that mindfulness can help to reduce the effects of all the stressors in your life by keeping you in the present moment. This not only helps move you out of anxiety, but also helps you accept the things you have been fearing. In doing this, new solutions may become apparent and positive actions are easier to take.

Gratitude

It is hard to overstate the importance of gratitude in both positive psychology and addiction recovery. This is because gratitude can have a profoundly positive impact on many other measures of wellbeing, such as satisfaction in life and better mental health.[18] Gratitude also increases the odds that people with severe addiction problems will remain sober in the long-term.[19]

You may recall that gratitude shows up as one of the core human strengths in the VIA list earlier in this chapter. Some mental health researchers refer to people who consistently display this trait as having "dispositional gratitude." This is different than what we might call "situational gratitude," which would be gratitude for a specific thing or set of circumstances in their lives. For instance, people who have strong dispositional gratitude tend to do better in recovery in general and even report doing okay if they never completely stop using alcohol, whereas AA members who are sober more than 90 days display situational gratitude that may be based more on having gotten their lives back than on having had a naturally grateful outlook before recovery.[19] In both cases, gratitude helps make lives better in both the short and long terms. In other words, whether you are naturally grateful or have to work at it, gratitude will bestow its benefits.

Like all the other strengths, gratitude is a skill that can be learned, like a muscle that benefits from regular exercise. There are many ways to do this, and they almost universally come down to taking the time to notice what is good in your life. As someone in one of my recovery fellowships likes to ask, how much time do you spend concentrating on what you *do* have instead of what you *don't* have?

One great way to do this is to engage in gratitude journaling. This simple idea can have a profound impact on mental health and positive outlook on life, even in people who struggle to find optimism or positive self-image. Gratitude journaling is often as simple as making a list of positive things you noticed in your life in the past 24 hours. Listing the same things every day can get repetitive and thus lose its power, so you'll want to mix it up a little to get the most benefit.

Here are a few ideas to keep your gratitude journaling fresh:

- "Feature Presentation" - Write a few things down each day, then pick one of them and write a paragraph or a page about what you particularly liked or appreciated about having this as part of your day.
- "I Know My ABC's" – Write something that starts with each letter of the alphabet. This might be hard to do daily without getting repetitive, but it makes a great way to get out of your routine. I find that an ABC

gratitude list shows me where my thoughts are that day. Hungry? "Apples, Bananas, Cherries..." Spiritual? "Altruism, Blessings, Compassion..." I have a friend in recovery who says they make an alphabetical gratitude list in their head to drift off to sleep at night.

- "Never Repeat" – Write a short list (3-5 things daily) but never repeat anything. In other words, if you have ever included something on your list before, you can never use it again. In a short while, you will have used up all the obvious things and will have to be on the lookout every day for new things. This will train your brain to be in a gratitude mindset, which is a great way to be.

- "Pace Yourself" – Write a daily list for 30-90 days, and then switch to weekly for a while. This will keep it from getting stale but still maintains momentum.

There is abundant research showing that gratitude journaling yields positive results, so try it out and see how it can help you. Practice more gratitude in general, such as talking about it with others and expressing gratitude for the ones you love, and you will likely feel a difference in your life even if things on the outside aren't getting better as fast as you'd like. This can be especially helpful as you move through the difficulties of loving someone who struggles with addiction. Having an attitude of gratitude won't get or keep them sober but it can help you find greater peace and acceptance for their journey, and for yours.

As you explore these concepts of positive psychology, find what works best for you. Try each one out to see what impact it has on your happiness. Explore any that inspire you, as there is abundant information available on each one. Enjoy!

Chapter 10

Concluding Thoughts

Throughout this book, we have looked at the elements of finding realistic hope. These have included education about addiction, what to expect in your loved one's journey and your own, and many resources and ideas to consider. Above all, I hope you have found inspiration to find your own recovery regardless of what your loved one does or does not do for theirs. From my heart, I wish that each and every one of your loved ones finds recovery from their addiction, but I know that neither you nor I have the power to make that happen. Give them the dignity of their experience and the opportunity to change if and when they are ready.

Where we can focus our efforts instead is on our own recovery. Pick up the tools you have read about, explore more on your own, find the fellowship of others who know not only the pain of loving someone with addiction, but have also found how to have joy and realistic hope for themselves. Turn to professionals where you find it appropriate. Above all, never be afraid to ask for help.

I wish you the best as you and your family walk the road of realistic hope. May you find peace and happiness along the way.

Love and light,
P. Casey Arrillaga, LCSW, LCDC
addictionandthefamily@gmail.com

Appendix: Resources for Family Recovery

Podcast

As of the writing, I host a podcast for family members, called "Addiction and the Family" that can be found anywhere you get podcasts, or at www.addictionandthefamily.info

Website

My site CaseyAuthor.com includes all of my books, videos, interviews, and anything else I can come up with to help people with addiction and their families find recovery.

Family Recovery Fellowships

Al-Anon (includes Alateen for teen members)
www.alanon.org
1-888-4AL-ANON (1-888-425-2666)
Al-Anon Family Group Headquarters, Inc
1600 Corporate Landing Parkway
Virginia Beach, VA 23454-5617
Telephone: (757) 563-1600
Fax: (757) 563-1656
Email: wso@al-anon.org

SMART Recovery Family & Friends

www.smartrecovery.org/family/
7304 Mentor Avenue Suite F Mentor, OH 44060
 Telephone: 440-951-5357
 Fax: 440-951-5358

Codependents Anonymous (CoDA)
https://coda.org/
Fellowship Services Office
PO Box 33577
Phoenix, AZ 85067-3577
Telephone (602) 277-7991
Telephone (888) 444-2359 (Toll Free)
Telephone (888) 444-2379 (Español)

Families Anonymous
www.familiesanonymous.org
Families Anonymous, Inc.
701 Lee St., Suite 670
Des Plaines, IL 60016
Telephone US: 800-736-9805
Telephone INT: 847-294-5877
Fax: 1-847-294-5837
Email: info@familiesanonymous.org

Thanks

Thank you first and foremost to the many people with addiction and their families who have honored me by allowing me to walk with you for a time on your journey of recovery. That experience was the birthplace of this book, including the times when one family member or another would ask when I would write something. I laughed this off when first asked, but without you, this would not exist.

Thank you also to my many mentors and professional supporters. These include (but are not limited to) Jackie Arcand, who first showed me how it was done, Heather Ingram, who helped me shape and expand a family program when we both were new to Texas, and both Shannon Malish and Melanie Little, who believed in me and supported me in creating the family workshop at Windmill Wellness Ranch. To Paige Majko, Ally DeGraff, Kristen Christopher, and Mia Tracy, I thank you for the good times co-facilitating family workshops. I learned from all of you.

Thank you to Michaela and Chris Kapilla, who championed this book, read drafts from the first few paragraphs through to the final stages, and have supported it in every way. Thanks to Sylvia Woods for editing prowess and kind words.

Special thanks goes to Kira Arrillaga for being a great sounding board, copy editor, kind counselor when I felt unsure, and of course for being the love of my life.

Finally, I must thank our countless anonymous foremothers and forefathers in recovery, who paved the early pathways of family recovery, and all those who keep the pathways lit today. Blessings to you all.

References

Introduction

1. Lindgren, E., Gray, K., Miller, G., Tyler, R., Wiers, C. E., Volkow, N. D., Wang. G. J. (2018). Food addiction: A common neurobiological mechanism with drug abuse. *Frontiers In Bioscience, Landmark, 23*, 811-836.
2. American Psychiatric Association. (2019). *What is gambling disorder?*. Retrieved from: https://www.psychiatry.org/ patients-families/gambling-disorder/what-is-gambling-disorder
3. Zhang, C., Brook, J. S., Leukefeld, C. G., De La Rosa, M., & Brook, D. W. (2017). Compulsive buying and quality of life: An estimate of the monetary cost of compulsive buying among adults in early midlife. *Psychiatry Research, 252*, 208–214.
4. Derbyshire, K. L., & Grant, J. E. (2015). Compulsive sexual behavior: a review of the literature. *Journal of Behavioral Addictions, 4*(2), 37–43.

303

Chapter 1

1. World Health Organization. (2019). *Management of substance abuse: Facts and figures.* Retrieved from: https://www.who.int/substance_abuse/facts/en/

2. Centers for Disease Control and Prevention. (2019) *About adverse childhood experiences.* Retrieved from: https://www.cdc.gov/violenceprevention/childabus andneglect/acestudy/aboutace.html

3. Lerner, J. S., Li, Y., Valdesolo, P., Kassam, K. S. (2015). Emotion and decision making. *Annual Review of Psychology 66*(1), 799-823.

4. Buschmann, T., Horn, R. A., Blankenship, V. R., Garcia, Y E., & Bohan, K. B. (2017). The relationship between automatic thoughts and irrational beliefs predicting anxiety and depression. *Journal of Rational - Emotive & Cognitive - Behavior Therapy, 36*(2), 137-162.

5. Roxo, M. R., Franceschini, P. R., Zubaran, C., Kleber, F. D., & Sander, J. W. (2011). The limbic system conception and its historical evolution. *The Scientific World Journal, 11,* 2428–2441.

6. Anokhin, A. P., Grant, J. D., Mulligan, R. C., & Heath, A. C. (2015). The genetics of impulsivity: evidence for the heritability of delay discounting. *Biological psychiatry, 77*(10), 887–894.

7. Sherva, R., Wang, Q., Kranzler, H., Zhoa, H., Koesterer, R., Herman, A., ... Gelernter, J. (2016). Genome wide association study of cannabis dependence severity, novel risk variants, and shared genetic risks. *JAMA Psychiatry, 73*(5), 472-480.

8. Reginsson, G. W., Ingason, A., Euesden, J., Bjornsdottir, G., Olafsson, S., Sigurdsson, E., ...Stefansson, K. (2018). Polygenic risk scores for schizophrenia and bipolar disorder associate with addiction. *Addiction Biology, 23*, 485– 492.

9. Blum, K., Oscar-berman, M., Demetrovics, Z., Barh, D., & Gold, M. S. (2014). Genetic addiction risk score (GARS): Molecular neurogenetic evidence for predisposition to reward deficiency syndrome (RDS). *Molecular Neurobiology, 50*(3), 765-96.

10. Bates, T. C. (2015). The glass is half full and half empty: A population-representative twin study testing if optimism and pessimism are distinct systems, *The Journal of Positive Psychology, 10*(6), 533-542.

Chapter 2

1. Adult Children of Alcoholics. (2019). *The laundry list – 14 traits of an adult child of an alcoholic.* Retrieved from: https://adultchildren.org/literature/laundry-list/

2. Al-Anon Family Groups. (2019). *Al-anon faces alcoholism: Help and hope for families and friends of alcoholics.* Retrieved from: https://al-anon.org/pdf/AFA2019

3. Spitz J. (2018). Addiction, spirituality, and resilience. In MacMillan T., Sisselman-Borgia A. (eds) *New directions in treatment, education, and outreach for mental health and addiction: Advances in mental health and addiction.* Springer, Cham.

4. S., A. (2014). *A narrative timeline of AA history: Public version for public posting.* Retrieved from: http://www.williamwhitepapers.com/recovery_mut al_aid_history/alcoholicsanonymous/

5. W., Bill. (1976). *Alcoholics anonymous : The story of how many thousands of men and women have recovered from alcoholism.* New York: Alcoholics Anonymous World Services.

6. Al-Anon Family Groups. (2019). *Al-anon history.* Retrieved from: https://al-anon.org/for members/wso/archives/history/

7. Mustain, J., & Helminiak, D. (2015). Understanding spirituality in recovery from addiction: Reintegrating the psyche to release the human spirit. *Addiction Research & Theory, 23*(5), 364-371.

8. Katie, G. K. (2018). Interpretive phenomenological analysis of the spiritual characteristics of recovery

experiences in the context of the brain disease model of addiction. *Pastoral Psychology, 67*(4), 357-372.

9. Newberg, A. B., & Waldman, R. W. (2010). *How God changes your brain: Breakthrough findings from a leading neuroscientist.* New York: Ballantine Books.

10. Forrester-Jones, R., Dietzfelbinger, L., Stedman, D., & Richmond, P. (2018). Including the 'spiritual' within mental health care in the UK, from the experiences of people with mental health problems. *Journal of Religion and Health, 57*(1), 384-407.

11. Trimpey, J. (1995). *The small book: A revolutionary alternative for overcoming alcohol and drug dependence.* New York: Dell.

12. Hasin, D. S., & Grant, B. F. (2015). The National Epidemiologic Survey on Alcohol and Related Conditions (NESARC) waves 1 and 2: review and summary of findings. *Social Psychiatry & Psychiatric Epidemiology, 50*(11), 1609–1640.

13. Al-Anon Family Groups. (2019). *2018 Al-Anon membership survey.* Retrieved from: https://alanon.org/resources-for professionals/membership-survey/

14. Peterson, C., Stephens, J.P., Nansook, P., Lee, F., & Seligman, M. P. (2009). In Linley, P. A., Harrington, S., & Page, N. (Eds.), *Handbook of positive psychology and work.* New York: Oxford University Press.

15. Tov, W. , Nai, Z. L. and Lee, H. W. (2016), Extraversion and agreeableness: Divergent routes to daily satisfaction with social relationships. *Journal of Personality, 84*(1), 121-134.

16. Kemp, R. (2019). Addiction and addiction recovery: A qualitative research viewpoint. *Journal of Psychological Therapies, 4*(2), 167-179.

17. Wiersbe, W. W. (2011). *On being a leader for God.* Ada, MI: Baker Books.

18. Center for Substance Abuse Treatment. (2004). *Substance abuse treatment and family therapy.* Rockville (MD): Substance Abuse and Mental Health Services Administration (US).

Chapter 3

1. Prochaska, J. O., & DiClemente, C. C. (1983). Stages and process of self-change in smoking: Toward and integrative model of change. *Journal of Consulting and Clinical Psychology, 51*(3), 390-395.

2. Hayes, N. D., Bradshaw, S. D., Mullet, N., Smith, J. A., & Shumway, S. S. (2019). Exploring family member influence on change in addiction treatment: A dyadic analysis. *Alcoholism Treatment Quarterly 37*(3), 377 395.

3. Walker, M. (2017). *Why we sleep: Unlocking the power of sleep and dreams.* New York: Scribner.

4. Peterson, C., Stephens, J.P., Nansook, P., Lee, F., & Seligman, M. P. (2009). In Linley, P. A., Harrington, S., & Page, N. (Eds.), *Handbook of positive psychology and work.* New York: Oxford University Press.

5. National Institute on Drug Abuse [NIDA]. (2018). Principles of drug addiction treatment: A research-based guide (3rd ed.). Retrieved from https://www.drugabuse.gov/publications/principle-drug-addiction-treatment-research-based-guide-third-edition

Chapter 4

1. National Institute on Drug Abuse [NIDA]. (2018). Principles of drug addiction treatment: A research-based guide (3rd ed.). Retrieved from: https://www.drugabuse.gov/publications/principle-drug-addiction-treatment-research-based-guide-third-edition

2. Haug, S., & Schaub, M. P. (2016). Treatment outcome, treatment retention, and their predictors among clients of five outpatient alcohol treatment centres in Switzerland. *BMC Public Health, 16,* 581-591.

3. Bliuc, A., Doan, T., & Best, D. (2019). Sober social networks: The role of online support groups in recovery from alcohol addiction. *Journal of Community & Applied Social Psychology, 29*(2), 121 132.

4. Luoma, J., Guinther, P., Potter, J., & Cheslock, M. (2017). Experienced-based versus scenario-based assessments of shame and guilt and their relationship to alcohol consumption and problems. *Substance Use & Misuse, 52*(13), 1692–1700.

5. Chisholm, M., & Gall, T. L. (2015). Shame and the x-rated addiction: The role of spirituality in treating male pornography addiction. *Sexual Addiction & Compulsivity, 22*(4), 259-272.

6. Kelly, J. F., Humphreys, K., & Ferri, M. (2020). Alcoholics Anonymous and other 12-step programs for alcohol use disorder. *The Cochrane Database of Systematic Reviews, 2020*(3).

7. Texas Health and Human Services Commission. (2020). About peer support services. Retrieved from https://hhs.texas.gov/doing-business-hhs/provider portals/behavioral-health-services-providers/peer support-services/about-peer-support-services

8. Coffey, J., Wray-Lake, L., Mashek, D., & Branand, B. (2016). A multi-study examination of Well-Being

Theory in college and community samples. *Journal of Happiness Studies, 17*(1), 187–211.

9. Zemore, S. E., Kaskutas, L. E., Mericle, A., & Hemberg, J. (2017). Comparison of 12-step groups to mutual help alternatives for AUD in a large, national study: Differences in membership characteristics and group participation, cohesion, and satisfaction. *Journal of Substance Abuse Treatment, 73*, 16-26.

10. W., Bill. (1976). *Alcoholics anonymous : The story of how many thousands of men and women have recovered from alcoholism.* New York: Alcoholics Anonymous World Services.

11. SMART Recovery [SR]. (2020). *Purposes and methods statement.* Retrieved from: https://www.smartrecovery.org/about-us/

Chapter 6

1. Codependents Anonymous [CoDA]. (2018). *Welcome.* Retrieved from: https://coda.org/newcomers/

2. Anderson, S. C. (1994). A critical analysis of the concept of codependency. *Social Work, 39*(6), 677-685.

3. Özakgül, A. A., Yılmaz, S. Koç, M., Buzlu, S., Türkinaz, A. A. (2017). Comparison of nursing and mechanical engineering students' codependency levels. *Addicta: The Turkish Journal on Addictions. 4*(1) 63–74.

Chapter 8

1. Vernig, P. (2011). Family roles in homes with alcohol dependent parents: An evidence-based review. *Substance Use & Misuse, 46*(4), 535-542.
2. Botzet, L. J., Rohrer, J. M., Arslan, R. C. (2021). Analysing effects of birth order on intelligence, educational attainment, big five and risk aversion in an Indonesian sample. *European Journal of Personality. 35*(2),234-248.
3. Zemore, S. E., Kaskutas, L. E., Mericle, A., & Hemberg, J. (2017). Comparison of 12-step groups to mutual help alternatives for AUD in a large, national study: Differences in membership characteristics and group participation, cohesion, and satisfaction. *Journal of Substance Abuse Treatment, 73,* 16-26.
4. Merriam-Webster. (2021). *Scapegoat.* Retrieved from: https://www.merriamwebster.com/dictionary/scapegoat

Chapter 9

1. Powers, J. Z. W. (2021). *Positive recovery MD.* https://www.positiverecoverymd.com/

2. Froh, J. J. (2004). The history of positive psychology: Truth be told. *NYS Psychologist. (May/June)*, 18-20.

3. Gillham, J. E., & Seligman, M. E. P. (1999). Footsteps on the road to a positive psychology.*Behaviour Research and Therapy, 37.* 163-173.

4. Chakhssi, F., Kraiss, J.T., Sommers-Spijkerman, M., Bohlmeijer, E. T. (2018). The effect of positive psychology interventions on well-being and distress in clinical samples with psychiatric or somatic disorders: A systematic review and meta-analysis. *BMC Psychiatry, 18,* 211.

5. Butler, J., Kern, M. L. (2016). The PERMA-Profiler: A brief multidimensional measure of flourishing. *International Journal of Wellbeing, 6*(3), 1-48.

6. Goodman, F. R., Disabato, D. J., Kashdan, T. B., & Kauffman,S. B. (2018) Measuring wellbeing: A comparison of subjective well-being and PERMA, *The Journal of Positive Psychology, 13*(4), 321-332.

7. Lambert D'raven, L., Pasha-Zaidi, N. (2016). Using the PERMA Model in the United Arab Emirates. *Social Indicators Research, 125,* 905–933

8. Khaw, D., Kern, M. (2014). A Cross-Cultural Comparison of the PERMA Model of Wellbeing. *Undergraduate Journal of Psychology at Berkeley,*1-22.

9. Wagner, L., Gander, F., Proyer, R.T., Ruch, W. (2020). Character strengths and PERMA: Investigating the

relationships of character strengths with a multidimensional framework of well-being. *Applied Research in Quality Life, 15*, 307–328.

10. O'Toole, G. (2021). *If we have our own 'why' of life, we shall get along with almost any 'how'.* Retrieved from: https://quoteinvestigator.com/2019/10/09/why-how/

11. Lichtenthal, W. G., Catarozoli, C., Masterson, M., Slivjak, E., Schofield, E., Roberts, K. E., Neimeyer, R. A., Wiener, L., Prigerson, H. G., Kissane, D. W., Li, Y., & Breitbart, W. (2019). An open trial of meaning-centered grief therapy: Rationale and preliminary evaluation. *Palliative & Supportive Care, 17*(1), 2–12.

12. Lien, R. (2020). *From meaning of service to psychological growth and confirmation of identity: A mixed method research* (Publication No. 2020:175) [Doctoral dissertation, Norwegian University of Science and Technology]. NTNU Open.

13. Peterson, C. (2006). The values in action (VIA) classification of strengths. In M. Csikszentmihalyi & I. S. Csikszentmihalyi (Eds.), *A life worth living: Contributions to positive psychology.* (pp. 29-48). Oxford University Press.

14. Harms, P. D., Brady, L., Wood, D., & Silard, A. (2018). Resilience and well-being. In E. Diener, S.Oishi, & L. Tay (Eds.), *Handbook of well-being.* Salt Lake City, UT: DEF Publishers.

15. Sadhbh, J., Shand, F., Tighe, J., Laurent, S. J., Bryant, R. A., Harvey, S. B. (2018). Road to resilience: A systematic review and meta-analysis of resilience training programmes and interventions. *BMJ Open*;8:e017858.
16. Kaplan, J.B., Bergman, A.L., Christopher, M., Bowen, S., Hunsinger, M. (2017). Role of resilience in mindfulness training for first responders. *Mindfulness, 8*, 1373–1380.
17. Hofmann, S. G., & Gómez, A. F. (2017). Mindfulness based interventions for anxiety and depression. *The Psychiatric Clinics of North America, 40*(4), 739–749.
18. Gulliford, L., & Morgan, B. (2017). The meaning and valence of gratitude in positive psychology. In N. Brown, T. Lomas, & F. J. Eiroa-Orosa (Eds.) *The Routledge international handbook of critical positive psychology.* (pp. 53-69). New York:Routledge.
19. Krentzman, A. R., & Finn, M. T. (2019). Gratitude while drinking, gratitude while recovering: A study of alcohol use disorders. *Journal of Recovery Science, 1*(3). 2-12.

Made in United States
Troutdale, OR
11/18/2023

14710338R00195